D1590143

A ZEAL FOR RESPONSIBILITY

A ZEAL FOR RESPONSIBILITY

The Struggle for Professional Nursing in Victorian England, 1868–1883

JUDITH MOORE

The University of Georgia Press
Athens and London

© 1988 by the University of Georgia Press
Athens, Georgia 30602
All rights reserved
Designed by Mary Mendell
Set in Pilgrim
The paper in this book meets the guidelines for
permanence and durability of the Committee on
Production Guidelines for Book Longevity of the
Council on Library Resources.

Printed in the United States of America
92 91 90 89 88   5 4 3 2 1

Library of Congress Cataloging in Publication Data
Moore, Judith.
A zeal for responsibility.
Bibliography: p.
Includes index.
1. Nursing—England—London—History—19th century.
2. Hospitals, Teaching—England—London—Sociological
aspects—History—19th century. 3. Nurse and
physician—England—London—History—19th century.
I. Title.
RT11.M66 1988   610.73'07'10421   87-5949
ISBN 0-8203-0955-9 (alk. paper)

British Library Cataloging in Publication Data available.

Contents

Acknowledgments   vii

Introduction: An Unknown History   ix

PART ONE   St. John's House
and King's College Hospital

1   The Form and Functions of a Nursing
    Sisterhood   3
2   Origins of the Crisis of 1874   11
3   Resolution of the Crisis of 1874   25
4   Doctors and Nurses in the 1870s and the Sexual
    Division of Labor   40

PART TWO   The Crisis at Guy's Hospital

5   The Issue of Authority   53
6   Public Debate   63
7   The Governors' Investigation and the Ingle
    Case   75
8   Collapse and Reconciliation   84

PART THREE   St. John's House and Its Council

9   Sister Aimee, Joseph Lister, and Dr. Hayes   101
10 The Council   118
11 Secession   132
12 The Nursing Sisters of St. John the Divine   147

PART FOUR   Conclusions

13 Status and Sex in Late Victorian Medicine   169
14 Prestige, Professionalism, and the Care of the
     Sick   180

     Epilogue   188

     Notes   191

     Index   209

Acknowledgments

This book was written in Oswego, New York, London, and Anchorage, Alaska and has been helped to completion by people and institutions in each of those places. It was begun in Oswego, where the Penfield Library of the State University College at Oswego helped me to read and copy its microfilms of the *Times* of London, the interlibrary loan staff tracked down obscure books for me, and I was provided with a basement study which gave me invaluable space and seclusion. A research grant from the SUNY Foundation enabled me to spend the summer of 1981 in London. Inez Alfors and John Knapp of the SUCO English Department were particularly supportive and encouraging colleagues.

The use of manuscript sources was vital to my research, and the staff of the Greater London Council Archives were unfailingly helpful, as were those of the Wellcome Institute for the History of Medicine, the Royal College of Nursing, King's College Hospital Library, and the British Library. I particularly wish to thank Dr. Frederick F. Cartwright for discussing St. John's House with me over lunch at the Royal College of Medicine and for making his manuscript on the Community of St. Mary and St. John available to me. Dr. Cartwright will not agree with all of my interpretations of the events of 1874 and 1883, but he has been extremely generous nevertheless. The Sisters of the Community of St. Margaret graciously showed me over St. Joseph's Hospital, while the Nursing Sisters of St. John the Divine welcomed me to their mother house in Birmingham and gave me free access to their archives and memorabilia. The exemplary dedication of these sisterhoods to the work of nursing and their patience, interest, and fair-mindedness in response to my inquiries gave me a first-hand sense of the tradition of independent service they embody.

My colleagues at the University of Alaska, Anchorage, have been extremely supportive of my work. The faculty of the College of Nursing and Health Sciences have invited me to present parts of my research at university and state nursing conferences and listened open-mindedly to a non-nurse, while my English Department peers have accepted my apparently unliterary subject as employing principles and skills central to our discipline. I particularly appreciate the action of my chair, Tom Sexton, in sharing with me his knowledge of Victorian photography and collections of photographs, including many *cartes de visite* portraits of nurses.

Other persons who have read parts of the manuscript and discussed it with me, to my great advantage, include Amy Katz Kaminsky, Elaine Dorough Johnson, Sandra Zagarell, Ann Colley, Dorothy Friedman, Frances McConnel, my mother, Vera Crosse, and my daughter and son, Neith and Dawson Moore. All of these have had to work against my tendency to authorial obstinacy, and I thank them now for what may have seemed at the time a thankless task. What errors and asperities remain I must admit to be my own.

Introduction: An Unknown History

A recent advertisement widely published in Britain, to be seen in such periodicals as *TV Times* and in poster form on the walls of London's Underground stations and clearly aimed, therefore, at the largest possible audience, gave most of its space to a picture of a little girl in nurse's costume curled up in an overstuffed chair with a much-bandaged teddy bear to which she is tenderly reading a story. The caption states, "The best nurses have the essential qualifications before they go to school." After this assurance it may be something of a surprise to discover in the fine print that "you could qualify as a State Enrolled Nurse in two years, or if you have 'O' levels as well, as a State Registered Nurse in three,"[1] but the discrepancy typifies much of the conflict that recurs throughout the history of nursing. Instinct, it would seem, is not enough, but at different times nurses themselves, their champions, and also their detractors have all confusingly claimed both that women had an inborn gift for nursing and that women who presumed to function in a sickroom without more or less extensive practical training either in addition to or instead of their putative natural talents were at best a nuisance, at worst a danger, to their patients. The problem, as Ethel Gordon Fenwick (1857–1947), one of the pioneers of professional nursing and the founder in 1887 of the British Nurses' Association, straightforwardly put it, is that "the Nurse question is the Woman question, pure and simple. We have to run the gauntlet of those historic rotten eggs."[2]

Once stated, the recognition that nursing is traditionally a woman's calling and has thus been affected by all of the assumptions and arguments that have dealt more generally with gender and sex roles seems obvious, but nursing still has been relatively neglected by recent scholarship on women. When two professors of nursing at the University of Wisconsin-Milwaukee put together a course on feminism and nursing they did so in part out of an awareness that many feminists tended to regard nursing as "the ultimate expression of the degradation of women." As both nurses and feminists themselves, however, they recognized "similarities in [nurses' and feminists'] historical and current problems"—even though they saw little corresponding effort on either side to "understand, include, or collaborate with the other."[3] Kritek and Glass's linking of historical and current problems points a way out of the impasse: a fresh look at the history of nursing must be integral to any informed conclusions about nursing today.

The beginning and end of most people's knowledge of the subject is the familiar and static image of Florence Nightingale at Scutari, the Lady with the Lamp, iconized in the public consciousness on the English £10 note, but like many other such potent symbols this one too conceals even more than it embodies. Florence Nightingale herself spent very little of her long career (she was born in 1820 and died in 1910) at hospital bedsides; instead, she used every means available to her to further reforms not only in nursing practice and education but also in hospital construction, organization, and administration and in the new fields of public health, sanitation, and preventive medicine. She was, moreover, not alone in her concerns but was merely the most conspicuous of a large number of nineteenth-century women who devoted their lives, with as much self-assertion as self-sacrifice, to these causes. Today, however, ignorance of this embattled history has too often led to its derogation, so that even in schools of nursing it has sometimes been labeled "mainly an intellectual pursuit—when their [students'] main objective is to achieve practical professional competence."[4] Marion Ferguson, analyzing the current inadequacies in the teaching of nursing history, labels the field "fragmented" and "lacking a central focus,"[5] while Malcolm S. Newby, like Ferguson a lecturer to student nurses, points out that nursing history has been regarded as even further outside the mainstream of history than "the histories of medicine and education."[6] Like Kritek and Glass, Newby noted as surprising the fact that "nursing history finds very little place in the pages of the emancipation of women"[7] and proposes a probable explanation: "Until recently there has been such an orthodoxy in nursing history that there has been no scope for showing the conflicts."[8]

An examination of three specific conflicts in this history, between nurses and lay administrators at King's College Hospital in 1874, between nurses and doctors at Guy's Hospital in 1880, and again between nurses on one side and doctors and administrators on the other at King's College in 1883, events with considerable impact in their own time and ones which I believe can also yield insight and inspiration for both nurses and feminists today, is the main business of this book, but a brief look at some of the received ideas that have for a long time discouraged the study of these and similar events among scholars as well as within the nursing profession itself can be a useful preliminary. Not only have conventional assumptions about gender made nurses historically invisible in the past, but assumptions about class and religion have tended to blinker contemporary historians—perhaps feminist historians, whose investigative premises tend to be egalitarian and secular, more than others.

The question of the social class nurses both come from and then occupy by virtue of their calling has been troubling at least since the early nineteenth century. The literary tradition's lurid picture of drunken and illiterate nurses (Dickens's Sarah Gamp is almost inevitably cited) as the pre-Nightingale norm is still widely accepted though little investigated,[9] and the entry of middle- and upper-class women, many of them with independent incomes, into the field in the latter part of the nineteenth century created a controversy that continued for decades, supporters of the "ladies" maintaining that their moral influence on patients (not to mention on doctors and medical students) would be superior to that of working-class women while opponents, many of them doctors, found that their class background rendered the ladies entirely too independent and indocile. As Brian Abel-Smith observed, considerably more forthrightly than the many nineteenth-century medical men who wrote on the subject, "many of the new nurses were of a higher social class than the doctors working in the same hospitals . . . and the doctors feared that these educated women would undermine their authority."[10]

The insistence of the lady-nurses, as they were almost invariably called, on their class position is from a twentieth-century point of view, especially an egalitarian and feminist one, something of an embarrassment. Nevertheless, we should not simply conclude, as Barbara Ehrenreich and Dierdre English did, that nursing education in the Nightingale era "emphasized character, not skills." The goal, in fact, was both, and "the finished products, the Nightingale nurse[s]," were not "simply the ideal Lady, transplanted from home to the hospital and absolved of reproductive responsibilities." If, as they maintain, "to the doctor, she brought the wifely virtue of absolute obedience,"[11] then the conflicts postulated by Newby and in fact still recoverable from the newspapers, magazines, medical journals, and hospital records of the period would not have occurred.[12] As Annette Kolodny observed of the women writers of the American frontier, "If we judge [them] by the ideological predispositions of late twentieth-century feminism, their aspirations seem tame, their fantasies paltry and constricted. But when analyzed as parts of the world in which the women actually lived, those same fantasies emerge as saving and even liberating." Kolodny urges her readers "to consider the social and historical contexts . . . [and] to appreciate the psychological fortitude required to evade the power and cultural pervasiveness of male fantasy structures."[13]

"Fantasy structures" may seem an inadequate term for the grim fortresses Victorian hospitals otherwise resembled, but it is entirely appropriate to the politicized atmospheres within them. As Abel-Smith indicates, the lady-nurses tended to assume, from the male medical profession's point of view, an intolerable autonomy of judgment and action. Florence Nightingale "had the determination to use every weapon she possessed, including charm, social pressure, and almost blackmail to achieve the objectives she had in mind,"[14] and her methods were not unique. "Agnes Hunt . . . took the drastic step of sending small-pox patients to put their complaints to members of the hospital committee"[15] in her efforts to force reforms on that unwilling body, and the legendary Sister Dora of Walsall (Dorothy Pattison, 1832–1878, youngest sister of the scholar Mark Pattison, famous as the rector of Lincoln College, Oxford, and as an alleged model for George Eliot's Mr. Casaubon) became almost notorious for her audacity—and her success:

> Over the managing committee of the hospital she considered it her duty to exercise all the influence of which she was capable. These were mainly men, well to do and actually engaged in trade, or retired tradesmen. . . . It was never her way to yield her will in matters which she considered of importance. . . . When every other attempt had failed, she would go before the committee and boldly demand that she might be allowed to carry into effect some plan to which she knew they would object. When she met with the anticipated refusal, she replied, "Very well, then, I shall go," and without giving her check-mated opponents time to say a word, she would march out of the room. She was perfectly aware that in a few hours they would entreat her to make her own terms, and do anything she pleased, except leave the hospital. More than once, however, they positively accepted her resignation, and began to look out for her successor. This indeed was more than she bargained for, but the result was the same, no second Sister Dora was to be found, and the matter always ended in her keeping her post.[16]

With doctors and hospital administrators all over England meeting with this sort of challenge to their traditional authority and habitual practices, it is scarcely surprising to find many writers on their side insisting that the subordination of nurses to an inferior class position was an essential condition of peace. An 1881 editorial in *The Lancet* is outspoken but not exceptional: "There is still room for improvement in the manners, and even greater scope as regards the modesty and obedience, of nurses; but we do not think this improvement is to be sought by seeking [*sic*] a better social position for members of the calling. . . . The notion of lady-helps may be dismissed as absurd, and the class of lady nurses will not be perpetuated. Nurses must always be *servants*, and they cannot safely be permitted to rise above that position in society. The more respectable they are the better, provided always that their respectability does not interfere with their obedience."[17] The danger perceived by the editors of *The Lancet* is clearly not that lady-nurses might be arrogant or insensitive to the patients who had to depend on them but that they would fail in submissiveness to their masters the doctors, and it was in fact the championing of hospital patients, at that time mostly charity cases, which was the most common root cause of friction and worse between nurses and doctors or nurses and lay administrators.[18]

The humanitarian values motivating much of the movement toward nursing reform—or revolution—in Victorian England often sprang from Victorian Christianity, and religious commitment and moral fervor thus become a third critical factor, along with gender and class, in determining the character of Victorian nursing conflicts. Some nineteenth-century hospitals were the descendants of religious foundations, although many were not, but by this time most of these ecclesiastical associations were in abeyance. The conjunction during the period, however, of increased Roman Catholic missionary activity, the Oxford Movement within the Church of England, such noted conversions from its ranks as John Henry Newman's and Henry Edward Manning's, and the founding, for the first time since Henry VIII's dissolution of the monasteries, of Anglican religious orders all served to fuel not only religious interest but strong religious prejudice as well. It is within this additional context of controversy that many of the lady-nurses of the nineteenth century had to function, since many of them entered the profession through religious channels by joining one of the proliferating nursing sisterhoods. "Sister" itself, in fact, became a loaded term, sometimes serving its accustomed task of designating a nurse higher in rank than or in authority over other nurses,[19] sometimes implying membership in a religious order, usually an Anglican one very scrupulously refraining from administering the vows that characterized Roman Catholic religious orders but adopting a distinctive costume and to varying extents in different orders a distinctive additional role as religious mentors for their patients.

Like social class, religious commitment tends to be seen today as a less certainly creditable and positive motive force than it was in the nineteenth century, when even its most determined enemies acknowledged its power. There is now, on the contrary, a tendency among feminists to treat Victorian Christianity in terms of its repressive effects on female sexuality while dismissing its compensatory power to animate and inspire. It is therefore necessary to make the point explicitly that nurses from sisterhoods were no more modest and submissive than those trained directly under the nominally secular aegis of Florence Nightingale, herself a strongly religious but independent and unorthodox Christian.

The case of Sister Dora is instructive. The youngest of ten daughters of a rural Yorkshire clergyman, she found her energies blocked by the assumption of her father that she could be adequately occupied at home, so that she was twenty-nine years old before she made her first break with the domestic sphere, becoming a schoolmistress although her preference was for nursing. Three years later, without her father's consent but not distinctly in opposition to him, she joined the Sisterhood of the Good Samaritan, a body which she never formally abandoned although she grew increasingly independent of it once she found her appropriate field of action as sister-in-charge at the cottage hospital at Walsall, a coal and iron mining center not far from Birmingham. The small Sisterhood of the Good Samaritan gave her little formal training in nursing and little personal support, but it did give her, as nothing else had, the means of escape from a vacuous home life and the occasion which she herself improved to become a heroic figure in the history of nursing for the skill and practicality with which she served her patients.

In keeping with that principle of service, she insisted upon "conservative surgery" in cases where amputations would have destroyed her patients' means of making a living and when more painstaking treatment could preserve useful limbs,[20] and undertook the very unusual practice of conducting "post-mortems to increase her knowledge of practical surgery, especially on the eye, where prompt action was essential." As her pupil and biographer Margaret Lonsdale commented, there had never been "a resident house-surgeon at Walsall hospital, and it became absolutely necessary that the nurse in charge . . . should be able to act as a surgeon in an emergency."[21] Nevertheless, a modest and docile nurse would have waited for one to be summoned. Sister Dora's zeal for responsibility was a function not only of her personal character but of the reinforcement given her by her intense religious convictions and was rather typical of the sisterhood nurses than an exception.

Clearly, the professional nurses of nineteenth-century England were far from the attendant angels of sentimental novels. They saw themselves more often as challengers of entrenched complacency, even cruelty, and the medical establishment generally agreed on their potentially revolutionary character, though not on the need for it. They furthermore showed themselves to be willing not only to complain to each other or to work by such traditionally feminine means as tact and patience but by confrontation and at the risk of their places in hospitals, and the record of these conflicts awaits rediscovery. As F. K. Prochaska observed in *Women and Philanthropy in Nineteenth-Century England,* "We are perhaps too prone to see limitations where the women of the past saw possibilities. The closer we come to their lives the more variety we find."[22] Even a case that never became a cause célèbre can illustrate the clarity and fervor with which these lady activists took sides. In 1867, at Lincoln, a month's notice was given to "our nurses . . . by the influence of the drunken doctor over his farmer friends, and thro' the anger of some of the governors whose mismanagement we had exposed."[23] This unashamedly partisan account addressed by L.

Boucherett to Florence Nightingale typifies the strong feeling controversies over nursing could and did generate even in small provincial infirmaries under minimal public observation.

In the sequence of cases developing in the next two decades in King's College and Guy's hospitals, however (that is, in the cases considered in detail in this book), publicity itself was a major issue and weapon. Occurring in two of the most prestigious teaching hospitals in the capital, they attracted the attention both of the metropolitan press and of the London-based medical journals. From these published accounts and from internal records of the hospitals and the nurses involved as well, the sequence of events can be not only reconstructed as it was experienced but analyzed so as to reveal both the circumstances as participants saw them and the beliefs about men and women, doctors and nurses, religious and secular authority, freedom and discipline that they brought with them. Since the issues that precipitated these conflicts, in spite of manifold changes at the level of style, have persisted unresolved to the present and the principles of all parties to them were both openly expressed and directly manifested in their dealings with each other, a close study of these controversies can illuminate analogous situations today and suggest at least lines of thought and perhaps lines of action to be pursued in them. The nurses at King's College and Guy's hospitals believed themselves to be fighting for principles extending far beyond themselves; we may find that they were fighting for us.

PART ONE
*St. John's House
and King's College Hospital*

The Form and Functions of a Nursing Sisterhood

The nursing sisterhood invariably called St. John's House after the parish church near which it originated[1] was founded in July 1848 as a "Training Institution for Nurses in Hospitals, Families, and for the Poor." Its earliest aims as set forth at the inaugural meeting were, in spite of its name, not exclusively medical but fundamentally religious and communitarian as well:

> to establish a corporate or collegiate institution, the objects of which would be to maintain in a community women who are members of the Church of England, who should receive such instruction and undergo such training as might best fit them to act as nurses and visitors to the sick and the poor. . . . It is absolutely necessary . . . that the proposed establishment shall be a religious one, and that all connected with it shall regard the work in which they are embarked as a religious work.[2]

From its beginning, the sisterhood's organizers and members sought "to connect the institution with some hospital or hospitals, in which the women under training, or those who had already been educated might find the opportunity of exercising their calling or of acquiring experience." They also established clear distinctions of class and rank: probationers paid £15 a year, while nurses received board, lodging, and wages, "and at the end of five years, if

competent and deserving, a certificate." The sisters proper, who
were members of the institution rather than employees, might
be either "residents in the home, paying fifty pounds a year, or
they might live with their families and friends. They must remain at least two years, and were expected to be examples to
the two other classes, sharing in the religious and professional
instruction and the work in families and hospitals."[3]

The sisters, with their substantial premium, shorter period of
service, and freedom of choice as to residence, were thus set
sharply apart from the obviously much more regimented
nurses, but the two groups shared the powerful bonds of gender
and work, so that class loyalties, when trouble came, were less
significant than perhaps all sides might have expected them to
be. While only the sisters held positions of authority they
worked side by side with the nurses in the hospitals so that the
two groups knew each other intimately, a condition not shared
by their male sponsors, who would not in any case have aspired
to it. The council of St. John's House were "a committee of
sixteen clergymen and physicians, among whom were many
noted men but with whom no woman was associated. . . . The
Bishop of London acted as President of the Society. The Master
[a sort of chaplain who gave religious instruction to the nurses
and conducted their services] was to be either married, or a
widower, and the Lady Superintendant [sic] was to regulate,
with the concurrence of the Master, the domestic arrangements
and the appointments of the nurses."[4] The first head of the sisterhood was Miss Elizabeth Frere, whose family was to be connected with St. John's House long after her own brief association with it (1848–49) came to an end.[5]

This rather elaborate structure, in which the nurses were employees of the council but took their training and their orders
from the sisters they worked with rather than from that largish
group of eminent and presumably otherwise busy men, while
the sisters made daily decisions without the benefit of ultimate
authority for them, remained substantially unaltered until a
final catastrophe in 1883, but it caused friction long before that.
In 1903 the St. John's House News ran a series of articles headed
"St. John's House in the Past," and while this publication had no

interest in raking up old hostilities it may nevertheless reveal them even in the midst of nostalgia. Quoting from an undated but early master's diary, it reports: " 'Oct. 10— Saw M—— E—— — candidate for the situation of nurse; well recommended . . . but appears too diminutive in person to discharge the duties of nurse efficiently; sent to consult Dr. Todd, who is of opinion she may come for a fortnight on trial.' " It may have seemed to the sisters as it would to many modern readers that the master in this case was making an officious judgment on the basis of a conventional prejudice equating size and strength. The article itself makes no such speculation but merely continues, " 'It was later found best that the Lady Superintendant [sic] should be responsible for many of the details which had first been undertaken by the master, but which lay more in the province of the lady of the house.' "[6]

As Florence Nightingale wrote in 1867 to Mary Jones, the current head of St. John's House and her close friend, who in 1854 had supplied six of the original party of nurses Nightingale took to the Crimea,

> The whole reform in nursing both at home and abroad has consisted in this; to take all power over the nursing out of the hands of men, and put it into the hands of *one female trained* head and make her responsible for everything (regarding internal management and discipline) being carried out. Usually it is the medical staff who have injudiciously interfered as "Master." How much worse it is when it is the Chaplain. . . . Don't let the Chaplain want to make himself matron. Don't let the Doctor make himself Head Nurse.[7]

The later history of St. John's House was to demonstrate in detail both the acuteness of this analysis and the importance of the power at stake. A year after Nightingale's letter Mary Jones herself left the sisterhood rather than compromise over it.

For the time being, however, the difficulties experienced by Miss Jones in organizing the supply of even a small number of nurses for the Crimea (although she was able to send an additional twenty in 1855) at first inadvertently fostered the sisterhood's growth. Demonstrating the need for more systematic

hospital training and for a less complex organization of authority ("there were no less than five different authorities and no
one definite head"),[8] these problems convinced the master as
well as Miss Jones at least of the need for fuller training facili-
ties if not of that for "*one female trained* head." Thus, when
the opportunity arose in 1856 St. John's House undertook the
entire nursing and household services of King's College Hospital. The step was described in the *Times* in the report of the
next annual meeting of the hospital's board of governors "as
having been attended with the happiest results,"[9] but for the
nurses themselves it must have been traumatic: " 'Many are the
stories told of the day the Sisters took possession; nearly all the
old staff, who resented the change, waited bonneted and
cloaked in the hall for their arrival, and then left at once . . . ;
by the end of the day the newcomers, who had arrived in clean
and dainty uniforms, were more like a set of sweeps or charwomen, in such an appalling state of disorder had they found
their wards.' "[10]

The St. John's House sisters and nurses soon became not only
an important feature of the patient services offered by King's
College Hospital but one of the routinely cited arguments for
support used in the hospital's annual appeals for funds. An ex-
cerpt from a letter from James S. Blyth, secretary, printed in the
Times on 26 December 1868, emphasizes their value in the overall context of the hospital's character and continuing problems:

> King's College Hospital being situated in a very poor and
> populous neighborhood where there are no wealthy resi-
> dents, the committee are compelled to look for assistance
> to the inhabitants of more favoured districts, and they do
> so on the following grounds. It is to all intents and pur-
> poses a free hospital, sickness and suffering being the only
> passports required. It receives nearly 2000 poor sick people
> annually, besides affording the best professional advice
> and medicine to upwards of 37,000 out-patients who resort
> to it not only from the crowded courts and alleys in its
> immediate neighborhood, but from all parts of London,

from the suburban districts, and from the country all round the metropolis. King's College Hospital was the first to avail itself, some 13 years ago, of the advantages deriving from that system of trained and skilled nursing, under the superintendence of ladies, which is now being generally adopted, and the benefits of which are now so universally recognized.[11]

Succeeding secretaries appear to have used Blyth's letter as a model, only updating figures annually, including the number of years of service by the St. John's House sisters and nurses.

The now thriving sisterhood, however, did not rest content with its apparently entire success with King's College Hospital. Instead, this new public position became the base for an expansion of its own services and influence. In 1866 it undertook "the whole nursing, catering, and cooking" of Charing Cross Hospital, serving 120 beds with "a staff of thirteen day nurses and five night nurses, with a cook, a kitchen maid, and a housemaid," and in 1867 added an out-patient diet and visiting service for both hospitals as well as the nursing of yet another institution, the Hospital for Sick Children in Nottingham. At the same time, the sisterhood's private nursing, which was its principal source of earned income, also grew greatly. By 1873, five other London hospitals had attempted to secure the services of St. John's House, but these proposals had been turned down by the council—not, it is important to note, by the sisters—on the grounds that "they could not contemplate" such a growth in the size of the institution.[12]

The council may have had more than one reason for resisting an enlargement of the sisterhood's membership. Despite their growth in professional expertise and public recognition, the sisters were becoming increasingly dissatisfied over internal questions of governance. During the years 1865 through 1867, the majority of them, who held strong high church religious beliefs, quarreled with the bishop of London, Archibald Campbell Tait, who was the president of their council, over the appointment of their chaplain. Perceiving an appointment in which they had no say as an imposition on the internal affairs of the sisterhood, they gave three months' notice. They offered to continue their nursing work if they could do so while being recognized as an independently contracting body, but this proposal was rejected as completely unacceptable by the council.

Tait, a sincere though rather unimaginative evangelical clergyman who was to become archbishop of Canterbury a few months after the end of the St. John's House controversy, found the council's position more comprehensible than the sisters' and accepted the report of the committee appointed by them to study the issue as resolving it. The report was dismissive. Concluding that the sisters' determination to resign made it "*less* necessary to examine at the present time into the grounds of their secession," it also alleged that these avowedly unexamined grounds "but feebly . . . explain[ed] the very decisive course which [was] being taken." The council's own reasons for refusing the sisters' offer, as they had to do with its own continued authority, were quite clear: "The complete independence of the Sisterhood which they now assert their determination to maintain would be the destruction of the whole plan of St. John's House."[13]

In an attempt to retrieve the situation by breaking the sisters' solidarity, the council accepted Miss Jones's resignation but insisted that before those of the others should take effect each of the disaffected sisters should have an individual interview with the bishop. The sisters agreed to the condition but at the same time wrote the council reaffirming their unity: "we beg it may be distinctly understood that as our resignation of our connexion with St. John's House was sent at the same time and with that of our Superior, we consider that in accepting her resignation the Council have accepted that of all." To Dr. Lionel S. Beale, the honorary secretary of the council, who was also a professor of physiology and general and morbid anatomy at King's College Hospital's medical school and a long-time supporter of their work, they were even more explicit: "Our Superior wrote for us as our head, we are entirely unanimous. This resignation is ours, we are acting in every respect as one. And the act of the whole Sisterhood is moreover the voluntary act of each individual member of that Sisterhood. Whatever blame the Council have attached to our Superior attaches equally to us."[14]

The bishop's statement to the council at their meeting of 10 January 1868 reported the complete failure of his interviews with the sisters. Not only did they refuse to reconsider their resignations, they also continued to allege a reason that apparently still mystified him: "He understood one of them to say she had understood that the Council wished to interfere with the inner life of the Sisterhood."[15]

Unacceptable as this description of their policies may have been to the council and the bishop, however, they had little justification for their refusal to recognize it as the sisters' central concern. Their obstinacy in fact seems only to have shown the sisters further dimensions of their grievance. The minutes of the same meeting recording the failure of the bishop's interviews include a letter from Sister Mary Jones dated 30 December 1867 which declared, "I am by the voice of the Sisters the Superior of my Sisterhood, and as such I must diligently care for the needs and jealously guard the rights of my Sisters. A constitution of our own is essential, and we must claim the right to regulate our own inner life."[16] It was now distressingly clear that this apparent difference of essentially religious opinion over the chaplaincy was also a struggle for power, although a group of religiously motivated women and a group of successful public men conceived that power in different ways. As Sister Laura Girdlestone, one of the seceding sisters, put it after the break in a letter to Robert Few, one of the sisters' most sympathetic friends on the council: "*You* evidently as a Council, thought much of the prestige of your name. *We* did not weigh it for a moment. It was absolutely nothing to us. . . . I neither took in the position of the Council, nor the machinery (cumbrous and complicated as it is) of S. [sic] John's House. . . . I looked upon myself as a member of a Religious Sisterhood with whose inner life a secular Council could have nothing to do."[17]

The impasse was total, and the council accepted the resignations. Sister Mary Jones and the six sisters and one probationer sister who had shared her position throughout the dispute departed with their integrity, while the council retained the name, the "prestige," and the "machinery" of St. John's House along with two sisters more amenable to discipline. Sister Mary Jones and her adherents removed themselves to Mecklenbergh Street and regrouped under the new name of the Sisterhood of St. Mary and St. John, with Mary's injunction to the servants at Cana, "Whatever He says unto you, do it," as their motto and principle. They remained a small but viable organization, enough so that in 1874 they were able to open a home for incurables under the name of St. Joseph's Hospital which is still at work today. Only by giving up St. John's House had they been able to act consistently on the religious principles that had led them to join it in the first place, and their later history suggests they were satisfied with their bargain.[18]

Without responding to the expressed need for a constitution giving the sisters a distinct role in their own governance or indeed revising in any way the regulations which had already allowed one dispute to reach the proportions of a crisis, the council now appointed a Mrs. Hodson as the new superior of St. John's House. The health of the new superior was so weak that she was unable to supervise the nursing of King's College and Charing Cross hospitals, which was now delegated to sisters-in-charge, but she was a reliable low churchwoman, even disavowing the title of sister. On 6 May 1868, less than four months after the departure of Sister Mary Jones and her supporters, the bishop of London in a special service in the chapel of St. John's House "admitted no less than thirty associate and probationer sisters."[19] It must have seemed to the council that their victory was now total and their policy accordingly vindicated. In fact, they had now either confirmed or brought into being all the elements of the larger crises that were to develop, in full public view, in 1874 and 1883.

St. John's House was from its beginnings consistently wealthy enough to underwrite the charitable parts of its work in hospitals and poor families. It drew in part on the private incomes of many of its members and friends, in part on its earned income from nursing in families, and only lastly made an occasional appeal for public support. In one such appeal on 22 December 1871 the treasurer of the St. John's House council, R. Randolph Robinson, proudly described the institution as now having a membership numbering "upwards of 100, consist[ing] of a lady superior, sisters, lay pupils, nurses, probationers, and pupil nurses."[1] He pleaded success, that is, rather than poverty as a reason for public contributions, and in that his appeal differed markedly from the otherwise similar drives regularly launched by King's College Hospital.

The hospital, in fact, lost few opportunities to remind the public of its financial necessities. Even at such a celebratory affair as an anniversary dinner in 1870 it was announced that the unendowed institution's average annual expenditure was in the neighborhood of £9000, with only approximately £3000 guaranteed by subscriptions, and the public was urged to assist not only with this chronic shortfall but with "the urgent necessity for completing the building and enclosing the front."[2]

While literally concerned with erecting a facade,

however, the hospital also suffered from more mundane problems. In the previous year, a request for an increased supply of sheets from Sister Aimee Parry, the sister-in-charge, had been turned down by the hospital's committee of management on the grounds that it could not afford them, and the problem had had to be solved by a donation of £50 from Mrs. Hodson, who later had to come up with a further £27, 8s, 8d to complete the fairly modest supply of three pairs of sheets for each bed.[3] While the relative affluence of the parties was never directly mentioned when the quarrel between them became public in 1874, one charge insisted upon against St. John's House by the committee of management was the excessive cost of the nursing services, and it seems possible that this accusation showed a resentment of the sisters' financial superiority at least as much as it reflected an actual problem.

The sisters, however, can scarcely have seen themselves as occupying a notably privileged position, particularly after the recent apparent rout of Sister Mary Jones. It was in the wake of that catastrophe that Sister Aimee Parry had been named sister-in-charge at King's College Hospital; shortly thereafter, in 1870, Sister Caroline Lloyd was appointed to replace Mrs. Hodson as superior. Both appointments, it is essential to note, were made by the St. John's House council, and it would thus be their own appointees who would ultimately defy them, but at the moment the nine sisters currently active were only tentatively a political body.

They did indeed take the occasion of Mrs. Hodson's resignation to send a petition to the council asking that they should be formally consulted in the appointment of her successor, but the council chose to disregard their request and to appoint Sister Caroline without their advice. She was evidently a popular choice, and the council offered further pacification in the form of a resolution that "as they are most anxious at all times to consult the wishes of the Sisters, so far as may be consistent with what they may regard as the highest interests of the Institution, they will further consider at their next meeting the subject of any modifications of the mode of appointment of Lady Superior in the future."[4] Despite this resolution, however, the subject went unmentioned at the next and succeeding meetings, and the sisters remained without a right of formal consultation in their own affairs. Satisfied in practice with the nomination of Sister Caroline and probably wary of the sort of conflict over principle which had led to the departure of Sister Mary Jones, the Sisters did not press the point.

If their object, however, was merely to get on with their work as nursing professionals this itself would now prove to be unexpectedly productive of dissension. The crisis of 1874 was for public perception a newspaper crisis, erupting in the midst of apparent smooth order, but in fact problems between the two institutions had been developing for several years from multiple causes, and the efforts of various parties to assign blame became in fact an additional complication, as it is still an obstacle to sorting out the actual issues and events. The sole twentieth-century history of the St. John's House sisterhood, Dr. Frederick F. Cartwright's pamphlet *The Story of the Community of the Nursing Sisters of St. John the Divine*, depending largely on the hospital's oral tradition, holds Sister Aimee Parry almost totally responsible for every problem that the sisterhood and the hospital had from 1869 to 1883. According to Cartwright, a long-time member of the King's College Hospital medical staff and amateur medical historian, Sister Aimee was simply "quite unsuited to her post; she was in many ways an estimable woman, devoted to the patients and the nurses under her care, and to the ideal of Sisterhood. But she was also the worst type of female disciplinarian, a cruel martinet who never knew the moment at which it is essential to relax, in whose vocabulary the word 'compromise' was unknown. Her morbidly suspicious mind, which translated the most innocent relationship between man and woman into potential sin, unfitted her for leadership of the complex society formed by doctors, nurses, male and female patients."[5]

It is extremely difficult, however, to find evidence substantiating Dr. Cartwright's conclusions. The records of the hospital's committee of management, which as it was the complainant ought to have supplied the evidence, instead contain only a handful of very minor disputes. Its minutes for 8 July 1870, for instance, record a reprimand delivered to Sister Aimee for putting a straitjacket on a patient on the previous Saturday evening, a time when few if any doctors would have been present to authorize her action, and noted but did not include a reply by her;[6] the incompleteness of the record is unfortunately typical.

A dispute about visits by the resident medical officer to the wards at night, which may have aroused Cartwright's suspicion of sexual paranoia on Sister Aimee's part, was resolved in favor of the practice of night rounds as such with a proviso that rules regulating them be formulated after an investigation by a subcommittee,[7] which in turn ultimately agreed that Sister Aimee's charges were well founded and that the residents had an obligation to supervise the attendance of the clinical clerks and dressers, who had apparently been left very much to their own devices.[8] Sister Aimee's objection—that the patients' rest was disturbed—seems in fact to have been humane rather than sexual, but the incident no doubt irritated the residents' youthful professional self-esteem and contributed to her unpopularity with them.

At the committee's meeting of 17 October 1873, a letter was received from the house surgeon, Andrew Duncan, protesting the fact that, on Sister Aimee's authority, a nurse had accompanied him behind the screen when he examined a venereal patient. Duncan's letter makes clear that his own *amour propre* and not the well-being of the patients was at the core of his complaint ("they [nurses] do not accompany the visiting Surgeon, whose representative I am, or the Resident Accoucheur, or House Physician. . . . I would ask whether the Sister in Charge has power to give orders to the nurses to direct thus the actions of the House Physician"),[9] but he damaged his own case by refusing to see his patients until his dignity was restored, and the subcommittee appointed to look into the matter, while it did not endorse the dangerous precedent of a nurse, however senior, giving orders to a doctor, however junior, still gave as its opinion that "the presence of a female on such occasions would be in conformity with custom, and desirable as a general practice."[10] These three incidents make up the entire case against

Sister Aimee that can be based on the committee of management's own records, and given its character it is not surprising
that when the committee sought to remove her it refused to
present its reasons.

In fact, while there was clearly some personal resentment of
Sister Aimee the grounds for it do not seem to have been those
proposed by Cartwright. In a report to the St. John's House
council on 7 November 1873 (that is, just subsequent to Duncan's letter and at a time when the hospital's committee of
management was both vindicating Sister Aimee's conduct and
pressing for her removal), Sister Caroline Lloyd strongly defended the sister-in-charge:

> the Supr. feels that it is mainly owing to Sister Aimee's
> unwearied efforts and unselfish devotion, as well as to her
> singular talent for superintendence that the efficiency of
> the nursing has been not merely maintained, under great
> discouragement, but has become very superior in quality
> to what it was in 1868, and that the Sisters and nurses are
> so strongly attached to St. John's House. The Superior hav-
> ing been herself a sister in the wards at K.C. Hosp: from
> 1868 to 1871, can testify from personal experience how
> great an improvement has been effected both in the nurs-
> ing, regarded as a matter of professional skill and in that
> scarcely less important particular—the moral tone and
> good conduct of the nursing staff.
>   The members of St. John's House now at K C H including
> domestic servants number more than 60 females, and the
> government of so large a body is a serious and very arduous
> task, and the Supr. can always feel the fullest confidence in
> the present Sister in Charge. The whole body of Sisters who
> are familiar with the special difficulties attending their
> work are of one mind on the question now pending[. T]he
> Supr. must therefore respectfully but most earnestly im-
> plore the Council . . . not to comply with the request of
> the Committee of Management.[11]

If the central issue of the crisis of 1874 were to be stated in a
single word, both the record of charges against Sister Aimee

and Sister Caroline's defense of her suggest that that word would be "authority." King's College and its hospital had been created in 1851 by an Act of Parliament which gave "entire management and superintendence of the Hospital"[12] to its committee of management without spelling out the technicalities of implementation. This power was taken with great literalness by what turned out to be a narrow majority of the committee as it was composed in 1874. Led by Major-General Sir Charles Daubeny and served with entire and zealous loyalty by J. C. Walrond, the hospital secretary appointed by it in December 1869, the committee undertook to enforce its authority on the sisters and nurses of St. John's House. It was in its own view merely acting within the terms of its legal mandate, but the council of St. John's House, most of the King's College Hospital medical staff, and most of its board of governors ultimately disagreed. The *Times*, more sympathetic to the St. John's House sisterhood than it was ever to be again, put their case without qualification:

> It has formed an essential part of the arrangement that the Sisters and their subordinates should be responsible to the Sister in charge alone, and that she should be responsible to the Lady Superior; who, in her turn, was responsible to the Hospital Committee for the quality of the nursing done under her directions. Nurses, like other people, cannot serve two masters. . . . The nurses, assistant nurses, and probationers are the paid servants of St. John's House, liable to be sent to any duty in the Hospital or elsewhere for which they may be required or suited. While in the Hospital, their positions may be compared to that of the persons employed by a contractor. . . . It is very forcibly argued that St. John's House, as an institution, could undertake the nursing of a Hospital under no other conditions, since any departure from them would destroy its responsibility and its own internal organization, and would reduce it to the position of a mere machinery to save the Hospital Committee the trouble of engaging nurses.

In 1871, at the prompting of Secretary Walrond, a new contract had been drawn up between the hospital and the sisterhood. The latter no longer had jurisdiction over any of the
hospital's essential household services, and the number of
nurses to be present in all wards at all times was minutely specified.[13] Walrond expressed a hope that "these arrangements
will tend to increase the efficiency of the domestic department
of the Hospital and at the same time, enhance the comforts of
the Nursing Staff,"[14] but the obvious political effect, in addition to the creation of endless problems of treatment involving
food and supplies, was to decrease the authority of the sisterhood. Scarcely three months had passed before the new system was itself under investigation, if not attack, by a subcommittee "to consider the efficiency of the present Nursing of the
Hospital."[15]

The policy of the committee and the secretary seems at first
to have been to soften every encroachment with some piece of
praise or concession. The appointment of the subcommittee
was thus coupled with an agreement that "the temperatures of
patients . . . might be safely taken by the Nursing Department,"[16] and at the meeting of the St. John's House council on
17 June 1872, at which Sir Charles Daubeny, at that time a
member of the council as well as of the hospital committee,
was present, the minute book records both a congratulatory resolution from the court of governors of King's College Hospital
(the body to which the committee of management was responsible) on the nursing and a resolution by the subcommittee
complaining of its cost and insisting that it be reduced or the
system of nursing changed.

By 1874, when the British Medical Journal published a "Report on the Nursing Arrangements of the London Hospitals," it
was found that King's College Hospital, with 172 beds, indeed
had the highest cost per bed of all the hospitals studied, while
Charing Cross, with 150, had the lowest. Both hospitals were
nursed by St. John's House, and the study concluded that "the
difference in cost is due solely to the difference in number of
nurses which have to be provided; this was settled in each case

by the Hospital Committee."[17] The authors of the report failed to find evidence that the system of nursing used by a hospital was decisive in its costs and therefore concluded that "the nursing associations [sisterhoods] cannot be accused of extravagant charges." If costs rose initially when a sisterhood took charge, this was probably caused by a laudable increase in hygiene: "A lady-sister's standard of neatness and cleanliness is generally higher than that of a promoted nurse, and this involves a more frequent scrubbing of wards, changing of bed linen, etc., with increased charges for wear and tear and washing." Some of the sisters' probable assumptions, however, were questioned: "To a lady, the ordinary diet of a hospital looks plain and uninviting; she forgets that it is probably luxurious in comparision to that which the patient has previously been accustomed [to]."[18]

Questions concerning diet and washing were indeed important in the controversy at King's College Hospital, usually as components in the costs the committee of management consistently represented as imposed upon them by the sisterhood. When the case became public, Sir Charles Daubeny, their usual spokesman, stated as the committee's first requirement "that a reduction of the payments now made for the services of the nursing staff of St. John's House shall be immediately effected so as to remove the very great disparity now existing between the cost of nursing King's College Hospital as compared with that of all the other Metropolitan Hospitals."[19] It would seem, however, that it was the committee's own arrangements that were now reacting upon them:

> The Committee of Management fitted up some place in the basement for a laundry, a place from which offensive steam has, we are assured, ever since ascended to the windows of the wards, so as to injure and annoy the patients, and which is so much too small for the wants of the establishment that the work is always behindhand. Sheets and other necessaries which are required in the wards in the morning are often not delivered until late at night, and when delivered are so wet that they can neither be used nor placed in store until they have been dried before the

ward fires. It is maintained that the change has produced a pecuniary saving. Whether this be so we cannot say, because the authorities have neither published an account of the cost of fitting up the laundry nor of the wages paid there.[20]

Even the *Lancet*, the contemporary medical journal consistently least sympathetic to professional nurses, sisterhoods, or women in general, reported that "in the course of a visit to the hospital during the current week, we were shown a bundle of something (called by excessive courtesy 'draw-sheets') the condition of which reflected very little credit on the laundry officials."[21]

With the publication of the *Times*'s critical leader the controversy was now public, to the evident dismay of the committee of management, whose behind-the-scenes strategy was ill-adapted to publicity. Sir Charles Daubeny, in his response to the *Times*, blamed "the Council of St. John's House and their supporters" for precipitating "the scandal, if any, arising out of a revelation of names" which the committee of management, "out of delicacy towards the ladies, have hitherto strictly confined to their confidential records,"[22] but when Randolph Robinson replied on behalf of the council that despite the committee's recent action in giving the sisterhood six months' notice to quit it had yet to make any charges against them Sir Charles backed off.[23] Instead of fulfilling his apparent threat he expressed regret at having been misunderstood. He had not, he asserted, meant that there was in fact any personal scandal to be revealed about "the ladies, . . . but I did mean, and do mean, that I consider it scandalous to introduce, unnecessarily, the names of ladies into public discussions and disputes." In keeping with this gentlemanly principle, Sir Charles explained that the committee's evidence against the sisterhood, which Robinson had requested to see, consisted of "papers and letters, and suchlike documents as the Committee, for various reasons, have from time to time been in the habit of *excluding* from their minute books."[24]

This allegedly conclusive but in practice inaccessible evidence was in fact never produced, either publicly or privately, nor were the names of the ladies ever given at any point in the public discussion of the case that now ensued. Behind the scenes, however, the sisters spoke for themselves and for each other, and their understanding of the controversy emerges clearly both in their letters and memoranda and in the internal correspondence of the council, the committee, and Secretary Walrond.

Unable to affect directly the contract under which they worked, the sisters employed at King's College Hospital focused their objections more directly on their working conditions, attempting to impress upon their council their need of support instead of further concessions to the committee of management. When the committee proposed in March 1873 that they should be given the names of the nurses, the sisters had no difficulty in discerning their purpose: "It is meant to be an instrument of undermining the authority of the Sisters . . . and breaking up all the present unity of the body. . . . It is meant to make the servants of St. John's mere tools in the hands of other masters, and to deprive them of all freedom and independence of action."[25] The sisters warned the council that "any further concession" would be "entirely useless" and went on to describe the situation in the hospital as those working there actually experienced it: "The whole tone of the representative of the Committee of the Hospital [Walrond] is such as to shew plainly that there is a set plan and purpose to harass St. John's workers and to undermine them by constant misrepresentation and unfounded charges. We, who come into constant contact with the Secretary in our work, cannot but be most alive to all this, and naturally from his constant residence in the Hospital, and intimate acquaintance with its working, he is most aware of what steps will thwart and unsettle us."[26] The sisters concluded their long letter with a strong statement of their lack of confidence in the support of their council, describing its behavior to date as "a breach of good faith" because of its failure to "require *proofs* of accusations brought against us in our work" and to "protest against unfounded and unproved charges being entertained and allowed to work quite a revolution in St. John's system of nursing—in order to make up a hollow truce with those who are inimical to St. John's."[27]

It was now March 1873; the harassment of the St. John's House sisters and nurses would continue for nearly a year before the council took a stand on their behalf, and the precipitating event was an insult to one of themselves, Randolph Robinson, rather than any criticism of or action against the sisterhood. Robinson's position was awkward: like Sir Charles Daubeny, he was a member of both the council and the committee, but his sympathies, unlike Sir Charles's, lay with the sisters. When the council, armed with information supplied by Robinson, replied to the committee's complaints about the high cost of the nursing that they had overlooked such obvious factors as the physical layout of the wards, their high rate of occupancy, and the proportion of serious cases treated, the committee responded with a resolution to the council asking for his resignation from one body or the other.

This was at last something too much for the council to swallow. Rescinding an earlier resolution to remove Sister Aimee from her post if they retained a right of appeal to the council of King's College as the hospital's parent body, they replaced it with one agreeing to do so only "on sufficient cause being shown."[28] This was the point, of course, consistently most urged by Sister Caroline, Sister Aimee herself, and the sisters working in King's College Hospital—the point as well to which Sir Charles and the committee could never quite be brought.

At the council's meeting of 9 February 1874, Sister Caroline presented letters both from Sister Aimee and from the sisters working under her. The first read in its entirety:

Dear Superior

Having heard from you yesterday evening that the Treasurer of this Hospital stated to you that *I* am the "sole obstacle" in the path of the harmonious working of St. Johns with the Hospital authorities, I beg immediately to place my resignation of the post of Sister in Charge here in your hands—

Understanding also from the same source that there are

grave charges made against me to the Committee and others, I beg of you to request the Council of St. John's House
to demand from the Committee of the Hospital a statement of these charges, and to proceed to a thorough investigation of the same.[29]

Sister Aimee's subordinates permitted themselves a more emotional statement but made the same confident appeal for
evidence:

We do most earnestly entreat you not to accept [Sister
Aimee's resignation], since no [other] Sister could venture
to undertake duties already sufficiently arduous, but rendered far more so by hinderences [sic] which have been put
in the way for some time past, as well as by those of the
present crisis. We feel moreover that it would be quite impossible to continue to work here without the assistance
and support of a Sister who by her long experience is so
eminently calculated to cope with the administrative difficulties of the post, and who has gained the confidence and
affection of both Sisters and Nurses, a most important matter in the efficient Nursing of any Hospital. We would venture very strongly to press you to ask of our Council, that
the grave charges said to exist against Sister Aimee may be
made known to, and thoroughly investigated by[,] them,
and at the same time that opportunity may be given us, if
necessary, to bear testimony in the matter. Our knowledge
of the daily work and occurrences in the Hospital and of
the rectitude of her character make us confident that Sister
Aimee need shrink from no such enquiry.[30]

Now that it seemed a real possibility that the St. John's sisters
and nurses would actually leave the hospital, the medical staff
decided to take a public position, publishing in the *Times* a
letter to the committee reminding them that it had already addressed a "remonstrance" to them on the subject (which is not
in their minutes) and adding now:

The success of the work we perform in your hospital, and
the welfare of our patients, are so intimately connected

with the efficiency of the nursing, that we look forward with much apprehension to the proposed substitution of a new and untried system for one that we know from daily experience to be thoroughly good. We earnestly trust, therefore, that it will be your pleasure to submit the whole question to impartial arbitration. If this were done, we should hope that some arrangement might be arrived at by which we and our patients would not be deprived of the valuable services of the members of St. John's House; or, if that be found to be impossible, we would then at least have the assurance, which we certainly do not now feel, that substantial justice had been done.[31]

Members of the medical staff signing this strongly worded statement were George Johnson (who was also a member of the committee of management), A. B. Garrod, John Wood (the only surgeon signing), W. S. Playfair, Alfred Baynard Duffin, and Lionel S. Beale.

Not signing was Sir William Fergusson, the distinguished but aging surgeon who was the only other medical member of the committee of management. Fergusson took no public stand during the controversy but was recognized by the sisterhood as an opponent, as a letter from Dr. Beale, perhaps the sisters' strongest backer both on the council and on the King's College Hospital medical staff, makes clear. Writing to W. H. Smith, a governor of the hospital who had counseled compromise as the sisters' best recourse, Beale rejected the suggestion with some indignation: "The fact is that many concessions have been made—We have conciliated as far as it was possible to conciliate without allowing St. John's House to be completely undermined and destroyed according to the caprice of three or four, but for the benefit of no one. Just enquire into the behavior of Fergusson and Walrond during the past two years."[32]

Fergusson's name was an important one. According to Dr. Frederick Cartwright in his biography of Joseph Lister, the surgeon who ultimately replaced Fergusson at King's College Hospital and who was also to come into conflict with the sisters of St. John's House, the fame of the hospital and its medical school from 1856 to 1874 depended on two things, its superior nursing and the eminence of Sir William Fergusson.[33] By the time of Fergusson's death of 1877, however, only three years later, he is described by Cartwright as having "outlived his greatness. He was an old man, . . . and he had become arrogant and conceited; he had fallen behind the times and yet refused to accept any of the great advances made by younger surgeons. His lectures had become nothing but boastful accounts of his own out-dated methods, and the students ceased to pay any attention to him. When he died, on February 10, 1877 [of Bright's disease, whose degenerative tendencies had probably been affecting him for some time], the number of students in the medical school had fallen to the lowest since the hospital was founded."[34]

The simultaneous occurrence of the nursing controversy and Fergusson's declining competence and reputation may have been more than coincidental. However, an allusion in another *Times* leader to a report that "a member of the surgical staff had expressed dissatisfaction at missing the presence of a nurse to whom he was accustomed"[35] refers to Henry Smith, Fergusson's associate, and the fact that the medical staff's protest was signed almost entirely by physicians, not surgeons, is a measure, perhaps, of Fergusson's still strong influence.

By the end of February 1874, however, behind-the-scenes stratagems, protests, and attempts at compromise had all largely failed: no group's power position was visibly improved, everyone's motives and character had been impugned, and at last the public had been alerted to the whole unedifying situation. As the medical staff had suggested, outside arbitration seemed to be the only course open.

On 27 February 1874, the *Times* notified the public of the annual meeting to be held that day by the governors of King's College Hospital, whose task it had become to find a solution to the now thoroughly embroiled conflict, and reminded the governors, if they should need reminding, of the seriousness of what was at stake: "The existence of St. John's House, or of kindred institutions, is essential to the proper training of nurses, a class of people whose services are yearly coming more and more into general demand. A hospital is practically the only school in which nurses can be trained, and hence the separation of a nursing institution from a hospital places a serious impediment in the way of the supply of a great public want, and can only be justifed by urgent necessity."[1]

In apparent agreement with this grave view of its responsibilites, the annual court of the governors of King's College Hospital, presided over with great tact by Queen Victoria's cousin the duke of Cambridge and attended by such eminent figures as former prime minister William Ewart Gladstone, appointed two outside arbitrators, Lord Hatherley and Lord Selborne, the two previous lord chancellors in Gladstone's most recent administration, to study the case and recommend a solution. Both men were known for their depth of commitment to the Church of England, Lord Selborne specifically as a high churchman,[2] which may have predisposed them toward some sympathy with the sisters of St. John's House, on whose council Lord Hatherley had in fact served, but both were as well men with a reputation for integrity and firmness and an undoubted capacity as lawyers at the head of their profession for assessing evidence and achieving administrative compromises.

One governor, indeed, reiterated the committee of management's contention "that there should be no co-ordinate jurisdiction in the management of the hospital, but that all management should vest in the committee. . . . he held that if the hospital was to go on properly there must be no *imperium in imperio*. There was an opinion abroad that the hospital was under the thumb of a semi-religious body," but according to the *Times*'s account of the meeting this speech was greeted with "No, no" and "murmurs," and the general tone was conciliatory.[3] The *Times* particularly congratulated the supporters of St. John's House, who had come to the meeting "in considerable numbers, . . . armed with a goodly number of proxies, and . . . prepared to nominate an entirely new Committee," for their forbearance in allowing the sitting committee to be re-elected until the arbitrators' report was received, a forbearance based on the general belief at the meeting that the committee had agreed to abide by whatever solution the report resulted in.[4]

Unpublished documents, however, cast a somewhat different light on the proceedings unfolding before the public. The council's willingness to fight the committee at all was quite recent and provoked as much by the secretary's arrogance as by any strong sense on their part of the difficulties experienced by Sister Aimee and the St. John's House staff at work in King's College Hospital. The council's repeated requests for "particulars of the *charges* and copies of the extracts from the confidential records . . . referred to [more than once by Sir Charles Daubeny in the *Times*] . . . in order that the Council may have an opportunity of enquiring into, and the persons incriminated of meeting[,] such charges"[5] were repeatedly refused, and Secretary Walrond in fact now took the position that the committee of management's actions were properly to be seen as mere self-defense. The documents now in the committee's possession would be, he assured the council, "used by the Committee solely in their own defense when the charges from time to time recently brought against them [sic] . . . come to be investigated, but not until then. The documents are being made ready not in any way as an attack upon the Sister in Charge, or any other lady, but simply with a view of showing that the Committee were justified in the various steps they have taken in relation to the Sister in charge [sic], and generally in regard to St. John's House, and to clear themselves from the accusations brought against them."[6]

With even the identity of the accused thus shifting before their eyes, the St. John's House council had perhaps little choice but to appear firm in the defense of the sisters, particularly when the adjourned meeting of the governors was followed on 2 March by a further letter to the *Times* from Sir Charles Daubeny, who now stated that the committee after all had *not* agreed to abide by the judgment of the arbitrators. "We did not admit yesterday, and we do not now admit, that we have made any false steps requiring to be retraced," he explained, and a companion letter from F. A. Bedwell added that he and those other members who had brought the original and still unspecified charges against St. John's House would resign, "though not in any spirit of irritation whatever," if the judgment of the arbitrators or final decision of the governors was contrary to their idea of the "principles of discipline" necessary to hospital management.[7]

In fact, the apparently sensational tone of the warnings given by Dr. Beale in his correspondence with W. H. Smith seems to have been justified. Identifying Bedwell as a leader of the "numerical majority" of the committee hostile to the St. John's House sisters, he had written both observantly and prophetically:

Of the intolerant, overbearing arrogance of this faction you can form no idea of if you have not been much about K.C.H. during the past two years. They display qualities which I shall not name but which in any struggle for supremacy upon Darwinian principles will I daresay be of

use. I consider the conduct of some to be simply dis-
graceful. I am content to be ousted by such victors if they
can oust me but nothing can persuade me that I ought to
be a tacit spectator of the persecution of those who are
doing their utmost to serve us well, by persons who having
an amazing notion of their own grandeur and infallibility
and power unquestionably sanction if they have not encouraged bullying behaviour and misrepresentation in
their paid subordinates on the ridiculous pretence that
what they call discipline, but is really oppression and of a
thoroughly vulgar kind[,] must be maintained.[8]

Smith, who had been at one time a member of both the council and the committee but as he admitted had "taken no part in
the management of the Hospital for the past four years and
very little of that St. John's House," claimed that his distance
from the scene constituted an advantage—"I can lok at matters more calmly"—and advised Beale to join in what he considered to be simple realism. "The majority of the Governors,"
he thought, would most likely "consider it expedient that the
authority of the Committee should be upheld," and he recognized no "concessions . . . so vast, so important in principle"
that St. John's House should not make them. His perception of
what could be asked of the committee was significantly different: "It is, I think, contrary to all experience that such a body
should capitulate even if they are in the wrong."

Beale recognized the worldly wisdom, even the well-intend-
edness, of Smith's assessment, but he still saw the issue as inescapably one of principle:

I quite agree as to the great power of a certain kind of the
opposing hosts and I will admit that someone at least will
have to be sacrificed in order to save the dignity of a body
which cannot admit that it errs. . . . Already some of the
votaries of the great goddess Expediency are discovering
the solution of the difficulty—If only a sister in charge is
sacrificed peace is to be proclaimed immediately and the
doves are to coo as before—Hear our case before you pass
judgment. St. John's will not be destitute of friends and

there will be no doubt as to their quality whatever their number may be. As you know, the best men go down with the ship if the ship goes down, and to go down is not always the worst fate![9]

Dr. Beale's correspondence with Smith and the committee of management's request for Robinson's resignation were probably the principal incitements to the council's arrival at the court of governors prepared with proxies for an electoral attack on the committee. It was entirely characteristic of the council, however, that it was easily persuaded not to use them, leaving the sisters and nurses to go on with their work in the hospital from mid-February until early May in an atmosphere of intensified suspense and hostility.

Even before the governors' meeting the committee had printed and circulated a report to them justifying what it confidently called its "Impending Separation from St. John's House." While still not giving "the particulars of the various difficulties arising in relation to the sister in charge," it did allege generally that Sister Aimee's "bearing and temper towards the staff of the Hospital and other dependents" had been the initial provocation for its decision, reinforced by the council's refusal to remove her when asked to do so: "The experience of the last eighteen months has confirmed the Committee in the opinion that the Constitution of St. John's House and the extent of the power and influence of the Council of that body over the Sisterhood with which it is associated are such that the Hospital ought not to enter into a contract with it which leaves it in the least particular doubtful that the Sisterhood is bound to 'obey' the directions given to it by the Committee of Management."[10]

The council, in fact, seems to have been held by the committee in that contempt which men sometimes reserve for other men who have failed to keep their women in line. If so, it follows logically enough that the report should go on to single out the sisters' independence as the characteristic which rendered them unsuitable for further employment. In the name of "responsibility," the sister-in-charge made decisions on the basis of her own judgment, and this could not be allowed: "The only way in which a Sisterhood can be associated with the work of the Hospital with advantage to the Institution, and with any hope of permanence, is, that the Sisterhood should once and for all understand that they and the nurses as a body owe 'obedience' to the Hospital authorities."[11] The committee, the report asserted, could issue any order without regard to the nursing staff's prior instructions or internal chain of command; it could remove any sister or nurse who questioned or disobeyed. Such was "obedience"; it was clearly incompatible with responsibility.

In March, acting apparently on her own initiative and not through the council, Sister Caroline addressed a printed but "Private and Confidential" letter to Lord Hatherley. In sharp contrast with the committee, she not only emphasized principles but related them to practice, explaining St. John's House policies in terms both of their reasons and of their effects, as on the exemplary disputed topic of how night nursing should be provided:

> In most Hospitals the night nurse is an inferior person, ignorant and incapable, often hired only by the night, unknown to the nurse who leaves her in charge, unknown to the patients and caring nothing for them, and knowing nothing of the very beginnings of nursing. . . . Our day and night nurses . . . take day and night duty in turn; if there is any difference, it is that the most trustworthy, the most steady, are put upon night duty, as being then left necessarily more to their own resources than by day. They have the same pay, the same privileges, the same advantages in their turn one as the other. . . . Great evils have been checked and exterminated by this plan; but, while in reality so excellent, it has one apparent disadvantage, which has been much exaggerated and employed against us. It produces the appearance of a change in the ward, for when the day nurse takes her turn at night, the doctors see a different, though probably an equally well-known face in their daily visits; although the patients have the benefit of the same care through the twenty-four hours as hitherto,

whilst the nurses themselves, both day and night, are restored and refreshed by change of scene and companions.

Having established the connection between the welfare of the patients and the well-being and morale of the nurses, Sister Caroline went on to draw the consequent contrast between the sisters and the committee: "A St. John's House nurse is not regarded by her superiors as a drudge, who is to be worked for the convenience of others until she can work no longer, and then cast aside as useless." Instead, as members of a community such as Sister Caroline only deemed possible as existing "between nurses and superiors of their own sex," nurses and sisters worked together with service to patients, a recurring theme in the letter though not in any of the many documents generated by the committee, as their common goal.[12]

With the premises on which St. John's House functioned now established, Sister Caroline went on to review the history of the sisterhood's relations with King's College Hospital since J. C. Walrond had been in charge of its operations. Walrond had been appointed in 1869, with no previous experience of hospital work but with an expressed prejudice against religious sisterhoods. Any merits he may have had were naturally enough not apparent to Sister Caroline, but she noted that he "soon gained a remarkable ascendancy over the Committee," which had dispensed him from the usual condition that he should reside in the hospital. The secretary's periods of absence had had practical consequences for the nurses and sisters of St. John's House:

> the headship of the establishment devolved upon the Steward, or upon the Steward's wife, or upon a boy employed in the Steward's office; all of them persons totally unfit for such responsibility. Their unfitness declared itself in many ways, and often to the detriment of the nursing by interfering with the supply of necessaries to the wards. . . . Each one of the complaints . . . entails upon a Nurse the extra fatigue of going up and down stairs, perhaps five or six times, before it is remedied, and thus compels her to be absent from her ward; to say nothing of the rudeness with

which she is usually treated by the officials, whose stereo-typed replies are that "she has had the thing already," or that the food "has been taken or spoilt in the ward" or that "the order was never sent down." Such statements as these have been proved to be untrue in every case in which they have been investigated; and the orders said not to have been sent down have been found, again and again, in the Steward's office.

As Sister Caroline made clear, these problems with supplies were not merely occasional sources of friction. Secretary Wal-rond backed his subordinates against the nursing staff, so that their initial "ill-feeling" soon turned to "open insolence" and once again not only the nurses but the patients suffered.[13]

Worse yet, when the St. John's House staff attempted to present their problem to the committee that body called their complaints "details" and sent them back to the secretary. As Sister Caroline commented rather bitterly, "Such a reference, . . . when it is made to the aggressor, deprives the aggrieved of any possibility of redress." Walrond also made effective use of his advantage, capitalizing on the committee's hint "to produce the impression that the complaints were unimportant, made for the mere sake of fault-finding, and also to produce the impression that the existing discomforts have been due to some personal unfitness on the part of the Sister in charge." As Sister Caroline saw matters, however (and this was the climax of her letter to Lord Hatherly), "The only fault of the Sister in Charge is her efficiency. If she were careless of her duties, and suffered the patients under her management to be wronged without re-monstrance, the Secretary and his subordinates would have nothing to urge in her disfavour."[14]

Finally, Sister Caroline included as an appendix to her letter to Lord Hatherley the text of a letter she herself had received from the ten probationer sisters currently in training at the hospital. It not only exemplifies the same combination of principles and practice as her own but also comes as close to a direct observation of Sister Aimee's personality as at this date we are likely to get:

We consider that our position here—constantly in our respective Wards, and yet exercising no authority in them—gives us peculiar advantages for appreciating exactly the relations in which the various members of the establishment stand in regard to each other, and for estimating fairly and independently the working of the present system.

We feel sure that the high standard of nursing in this Hospital, and the individual and affectionate care bestowed upon each patient, could only be maintained by means of an organized nursing body, under a Sister in charge, thoroughly acquainted with the minute details of the work, and with the character of the workers; and we also believe that the order and punctuality pervading all the arrangements of St. John's, the thoroughness of the nursing in each individual case, and the refinement and perfect neatness to be traced throughout the Wards, are due chiefly to the influence of the present Sister in Charge, who is so peculiarly fitted to the post assigned to her. . . . Her talents for organization and government, her calm gentleness, and her generosity and breadth of mind in dealing with all varieties of character, make her singularly suited for her very difficult position, while her power of evoking personal attachment secures such obedience as love alone can procure.[15]

The Sister Aimee known to patients, nurses, and her fellow sisters and the Sister Aimee complained of by the committee of management seem scarcely to have been the same woman. Meanwhile the actual Sister Aimee was, by the time her future at King's College Hospital was under formal arbitration, showing signs of strain. At the meeting of the St. John's House council of 26 March 1874 a letter from Secretary Walrond was read informing the council, with evident enjoyment of the contretemps, that Sister Aimee had had some "bed commodes" ordered by the committee taken away again as she had not been properly informed about them—"The Sister in Charge at once stated that she refused altogether to recognize the use or the existence of these Commodes; that they had been ordered without any consultation with her; that she considered such a course to be a direct insult to her as the head of the Nursing Department." Walrond admitted rather passingly that he had in fact given her no official notice, but Sister Aimee's show of temper was the principal subject of his letter, and the council clearly saw that, not the disposition of the bed commodes, as the problem they were obliged to respond to. After some debate they resolved on a politic answer: "The Council of St. John's House, although satisfied after enquiry that the matters related in the Report are in some points capable of being viewed in a different light than that in which they there appear, regret that a question of this nature should arise at a moment when, by the express direction of the Corporation of Governors, both parties are bound to use their best endeavours to secure a continuance of the present system of nursing, and they deprecate any discussion during the pending reference."[16] Some members of the council voted to delete the slightly combative, or at least defensive, "although" clause, but conciliation was no longer always the rule on the council, and the resolution passed unamended.

Sister Caroline, meanwhile, continued to see the differences between St. John's House and the hospital committee and its chosen representative as profound, and the bed commode incident, trivial as it seemed, did nothing to change her mind. While she expressed regret for Sister Aimee's expression of anger she also pointed out the secretary's irregularity of procedure and then proceeded to comment on the significance of this latest dispute:

> Things, that may be individually trifling, yet when of frequent and almost daily occurrence do have an injurious effect and certainly tend to place the Sisters in a very difficult and invidious position before the nurses and also before the patients[,] who do not fail to remark on what passes around them.
>
> It must be remembered that the nursing work in itself, occupying from 12 to 14 hours out of the 24, is a sufficient strain on all the powers of both mind and body and that it

is hardly to be expected in addition that injurious opposition . . . should be invariably met by unruffled calmness
and a serene temper.

I do entreat the Council to take prompt measures to
close the connection with King's College Hospital as I do
much fear, what would be a far greater evil, the general
break up of the Sisterhood and of St. John's House.[17]

At last, however, on 2 May, the adjourned meeting of the
governors was reconvened to receive the report of the arbitrators. Lord Hatherley and Lord Selborne, representing
themselves as advisors and disavowing "any impressions,
favourable or otherwise[,] to either party, with respect to any
particular matters which may have been, at any time before
the reference to us, in controversy," even though they had
"been in communication with both sides . . . [and] obtained
useful information" from them, now tacitly rested their recommendations for the future on the questionable premise that no
irreparable steps had yet been taken by any person or group on
either side. The controversy, that is, had arisen from a mere
confusion of jurisdiction between the committee of management and the sister-in-charge and from good intentions on both
sides "with, perhaps, some aggravation from personal irrita-
tions and misunderstandings, traceable originally to these
[essentially innocent] causes." The referees then gave it as their
legal opinion, first, that the 1851 Act of Parliament "applies
only to those persons who are, in the proper sense of the words,
officers, servants, or agents of King's College Hospital, and that
the sister in charge and nurses are officers, servants, or agents,
not of King's College Hospital, but of St. John's House," and
that therefore the committee of management did not in fact
possess the dismissal power which it had attempted to exercise.[18]

With "co-ordinate jurisdiction" thus established as an on-
going condition of the hospital's life, the two arbitrators proceeded to recommend some practical steps to make the sharing
of responsibility free of friction. "Matters of domestic economy" should be returned to the jurisdiction of a matron nomi-

nated by St. John's House; "one permanent resident medical officer" should be appointed either instead of or superior to the young men "of constantly varying characters and personal qualities" who now held the post in six-month appointments; and the nurses should wear name-tags or numbers. Neither the status nor the responsibilities of the nursing staff were to be in any way diminished.

The report itself seems anticlimactic after the months of hostility revealed by the council's minute book and the lady superior's reports, and the resolution of Canon Barry, the principal of King's College, that it be "accepted . . . as the basis of a new agreement between the Hospital and St. John's House, and that it be an instruction to the Committee of Management to carry it out," though cheered, was also debated. According to Barry, "A pamphlet had been issued by the Vice-Chairman of the Committee [Sir Charles Daubeny] . . . urging that the report should be set aside" and copies circulated to the governors, but Barry maintained that the majority of dissidents on the committee was slender, and that no real reasons for rejecting the report—or feasible course to follow if such a rejection were made—existed. His seconder, Sir W. Heathcote, went so far as to say that "he thought those who put forth the pamphlet . . . were placing the interests of the institution in great jeopardy. It would be impossible to carry on . . . if it should be seen that the difficulties were referred to two noblemen and their report put aside as waste paper."[19]

The Sisters' opponents were unmoved. Mr. Williamson, moving an amendment to Canon Barry's resolution which in effect cancelled it, complained again bitterly "of the excess of washing carried out by the sisters, . . . 23 pieces per bed per week, while the average of other hospitals was but nine. He declared that such was the cost of nursing in the hospital that the institution was going to ruin as fast as possible." The duke of Cambridge, again presiding, reprimanded Williamson for the "ungracious part" taken by his amendment, but Mr. Denison, Q.C. at once proposed an alternative one referring the report to the committee "to carry it out as far as they thought expedient for the interests of the Hospital." The duke of Westminster, however, pointed out that since the committee's position was already quite clear this would be only a waste of time, and the meeting ended with the rejection of Denison's amendment and the passage of Barry's original resolution.[20]

On 8 May the thirteen dissenting members of the committee of management again addressed themselves to the public through the *Times*. They justified their tactic of circulating a pamphlet to the governors before the meeting as merely more efficient than oral argumentation, disavowed any intention of finding fault with the report or its authors, yet still insisted that "we could not advise the governors to accept it."[21] Their position was completely unchanged and in fact unchangeable, and a week later the *Times* reported their resignation.

The council now consulted Sister Caroline about the best implementation of the referees' report and received a carefully considered response. With regard to the recommendation " 'that a matron should be appointed if possible on the nomination of St. John's House,' & &," she wrote, "it would appear that the most suitable, indeed the only person who could well fall in with this recommendation would be the Sister in Charge, who would then be nominated by St. John's House and appointed by the Hospital Committee." With this declaration of belief in both Sister Aimee's administrative capacity and her personal suitability at the very beginning of her report, the lady superior went on to consider the rest of the referees' recommendations in the same spirit: "I can only express my intention . . . of accepting [them] with such modifications, as the Council may deem most fitting—Trusting they will kindly remember that [the list of the nurses' names] is on several grounds distasteful to the Nursing Staff and that in especial regard to the feelings of the nurses (or prejudices if they be so considered) the recommendation may be carried out in such a way as shall not place the information at the command of any hospital official."[22]

On 27 May a joint meeting of the council and the reconstituted committee of management was recorded in the council's minute book. Agreeing to take Sister Caroline's report "generally for their guidance," they also received her further advice "to guard against any agreement by which the Matron should be rendered independent of the Sister in Charge . . . and that the Sister in Charge shall keep the roll of names."[23] According to the *Times*, "In dealing with a friendly committee the Council and Sisters of St. John's House no longer feel themselves bound to stand upon the defensive against any possible aggression, and they have shown, since the resignation of their opponents, every desire to approach the matter at issue in a candid and conciliatory spirit."[24] The manuscript evidence, however, shows that this candor was highly cautious. The doves of Dr. Beale's letter were becoming as wise as serpents.

On 19 June the *Times* reported the terms of the new contract between the two institutions. The hospital was to pay St. John's House £1500 per year for a staff of 34 nurses; it would also pay £650 for domestic services and £625 for "washing and mending of linen, etc., and cleaning of bedding." The sisters, including Sister Aimee, whose new title was sister-matron, were not paid. St. John's House would also receive "the opportunity . . . of carrying on the work of training nurses" in the hospital and—what the whole quarrel had at bottom been about—the responsibility of supervising its own staff. Furthermore, in a test of strength Sister Aimee Parry, strongly supported by the superior, other sisters, and her subordinate staff at the hospital and somewhat less vigorously by the council of St. John's House and by a majority of the governors and medical staff of the hospital, had maintained her position and that of the sisterhood she represented as independent professionals, while her opponents, who whatever merits their case may have had certainly handled them badly, were obliged, if only by their own political ineptitude, to resign completely from all connection with the hospital.

Even if the committee, however, owed much of its failure to its own folly, it is difficult to believe either that Sister Aimee's support would have been so great or her triumph so complete if her "bearing and temper" had been so defective as the committee claimed. The fact that the recommendation of Lord Hatherley and Lord Selborne that a matron be nominated by St. John's House to take charge of the hospital's domestic services was met in practice by the appointment of Sister Aimee to both posts was not, after all, an accident but a deliberate action based on Sister Caroline's strongly worded advice. The controversy had been, even though the committee's alleged secret evidence had never been presented, very minutely aired and investigated, and the referees had been definite in their dismissal of questions of personality as essentially irrelevant to the real issue of governance. If Sister Aimee had been the "cruel martinet" of Cartwright's description, evidence of that ought to have been available to such an extent as to have had some weight in the referees' recommendations—Walrond's effort to make an issue of the bed commode incident suggests that it was not.

In spite of the apparently peaceful solution of its difficulties, however, King's College Hospital now entered a difficult period. The embarrassing publicity of 1874 cost the hospital subscribers and reputation, and the fading of the medical school's chief luminary, Sir William Fergusson, also affected enrollments. Nevertheless, King's College Hospital and St. John's House worked on together harmoniously enough till 1882–83, when a new crisis developed. Its very different conclusion, the "secession" of the sisterhood not only from the hospital but from the government of the council and their own established residence in Norfolk Street, Strand, reflects not only changes in the particular circumstances of the case but the vicissitudes of professional nursing in other hospitals, in the opinion of the medical profession, and in the public eye during the intervening decade.

Doctors and Nurses in the 1870s and the Sexual Division of Labor

The medical profession in the second half of the nineteenth century was under pressure in a number of different ways. Its social prestige was rising but still insecure, inferior to that of the clergy, military and naval officers, and barristers, and its professional successes still occurred in a general context of high death rates, scientific controversy and confusion, and some public skepticism. In addition, its numbers were rapidly increasing ("by 53% in the thirty years after 1861, from 17,300 to 26,500")[1] a circumstance which caused some self-congratulation but also considerable anxiety over a perceived competition for patients, prestige, and fees. Although there were only 59 doctors per 100,000 people in Britain in 1881 compared to 100 per 100,000 in 1975, when the general health of the population made the need for medical attention less acute and increased mobility made access to it easier,[2] doctors during this period were apt to feel themselves not only insufficiently appreciated but dangerously thick on the ground.

In 1884 the *Times*'s leading article on the opening of the fall session of the capital's medical schools took for granted the existence of an "army of medical men doomed to languish in poverty and obscurity," a phenomenon resulting from an apparently unstoppable "superabundant influx into the profession."[3] In addition, the fairly common fear that the limits of their professional advance were about to be reached made medical men both defensive and anxious. Consider, for example, the surgeon J. E. Ericksen of University College Hospital who wrote in 1873, "That there must be a final limit to development in this department of our profession there can be no doubt. . . . There cannot always be fresh fields of conquest for the knife. . . . That we have nearly, if not quite, reached these final limits, there can be little question."[4]

That these various subjective perceptions were not well supported by evidence seems to have been little realized. Citing a study by Sir James Paget (1814–1899) of the careers of 1,000 of his own students in the medical school of St. Bartholomew's Hospital at about this time, G. H. Duckworth, author under Charles Booth's editorial supervision of the chapter on employment in law and medicine in Booth's Life and Labour of the People of London, notes that 596 achieved fair or better than fair success at their profession and 124 "very limited success." Only 56 failed entirely, the other 224 having either died or left the profession for some other way of life. According to Duckworth, "If we deduct the loss by death (which agrees with the general average mortality of males over nineteen years of age) and those who, after leaving the profession, succeeded in some other way, the proportion of failures and even of those whose success was 'very limited' is certainly not large," and Duckworth concludes his discussion by quoting approvingly Paget's own judgment in his study: "'All my recollections would lead me to tell that every student may draw from his daily life a very likely forecast of his life in practice; for it will depend on himself a hundredfold more than on circumstance.'"[5]

In general, however, doctors looked beyond themselves for someone to blame for their professional discontents, and the improvement in the training and status of nurses was frequently identified as a threat. The number of nurses was also increasing, but no one seems to have thought there were simply too many of them—it was the change in their status that posed the danger. Sir Edward Cook summed up the change in his 1914 biography of Florence Nightingale: "In 1861 there were 27,618 nurses 'in hospitals, and nurses not apparently domestic servants,' and they were enumerated, in the tables of Occupations of the People, under the head of Domestic. In 1901 there were 64,214 nurses, and they were enumerated under the head of Medicine." Cook went on to quote a passage from Charles Booth that probably states a widely held opinion and as such voices a potential menace to the authority of doctors: "The value of Hospitals as schools of surgery and medicine is hardly greater than is their usefulness as a training for nurses, and the field is no less large. . . . This change is perhaps the best fruit the past half century has to show."[6]

In an analogous situation, fear that midwives would capture valuable paying patients for many years blocked passage of a Midwives' Registration Act.[7] Even the success of district nursing, which at first aroused little opposition because of its concentration on the poor, eventually provoked the same response:

> fear that the ministrations of the district nurses might diminish calls on the medical profession and in so doing diminish medical incomes. . . . One member of the [Penwith Medical] Union complained that nurses attended minor cases of cuts and burns, thus depriving doctors of work. Another complained that the nurses were not competent to judge whether a doctor was needed or not. "It was reversing the natural order of things," he said, "that the nurse should send for the doctor; it should always be the other way round." His fellow members had "made up their minds not to go if sent for by a nurse, unless the rules were altered." And there was always the danger that the nurse might influence the patient in the choice of a doctor. This must be stopped.[8]

The fact that these complaints were made in the first decade of the twentieth century shows both the persistence of the doctors' fears and perhaps also an actual increase in them, from a fear of competition within metropolitan hospitals—obviously a high-stress environment to begin with—to the same fear in isolated rural districts.

If doctors, however, were dubious, the general public seems not only to have benefited from the better education and increasing numbers of nurses but also to have been aware of the advantages they received. For the first time in their history, hospitals became places where middle-class and wealthy people wanted to be treated instead of merely the traditional last resort of the indigent. In a leading article of 27 February 1877 the *Times* addressed itself to the question, "why should Hospitals . . . be only for the poor? Why not for all classes?" and expatiated on the newly discovered inconveniences of being ill at home, attended by the amateur nursing of one's female relations.[9] A later article the same year was overtly envious of what it presented as the typical patient in a voluntary hospital: such a person was "no longer . . . simply . . . to be charitably received and assisted. [Instead, h]e is a natural specimen of disease upon whom all the resources of medical art and science are to be lavished." The attention such an (as the *Times* implies) over-valued patient received would be "scarcely less than that bestowed on a Prince. . . . He will often, in these days, have the most refined hands to nurse him; and the great physicians of the day, who may be unable to spare time to call on some of their wealthier patients who are able to pay them, will on no account neglect their daily visit to the Hospital."[10]

The suspicions of the leader writer, through their display of class bias, constitute further evidence of the status revolution going on in Victorian hospitals; the outcome of the revolution, however, continued to be doubtful. Certainly the position of nurses as reliable care-givers, however refined their hands, was still hedged with cautions. In another leading article rather vaguely advocating their training in other milieus as well as hospitals (something it had dismissed as virtually impossible in 1874), the *Times* gave a character sketch of the sort of women suited to this training:

> They are sympathetic and gentle; they have no excessive flow of spirits or range of ideas; they can speak when spoken to, and hold their tongues when it is fit to be silent. They can attend to small matters and bear them in mind. They can take pleasure in small arrangements, so as they have a use or priority. They can attach significance to such

superficial matters as dirt or smell. They can believe there is something in orders which they cannot themselves understand. They can mediate between the doctor and the patient, being a faithful assistant to the former, and a kind, but not oppressive, friend and adviser to the latter.

Training, nevertheless, is still needed to prevent these paragons of docility from being "the baneful source of all kinds of social degeneration, from simple slovenliness and idleness to the more serious forms of vice,"[11] and it seems obvious that the reason for this otherwise incongruous suspicion is their sex.

Although the *Times* took what it no doubt believed to be a moderate and rational position on the new educational and political ventures of women in the latter half of the nineteenth century, it consistently and vehemently opposed all moves for the extension of the franchise to women, and its concession that there might in future be "a certain admixture of women in the liberal professions" was made only on the understanding that this would occur "without changing the relations of society and setting sex against sex. . . . The 'higher education of women,' when it is fully developed will, if it be worth the name, make women not less, but more womanly."[12] This proposal to use women's education to reinforce their nature, which was evidently not believed to have the binding force of other natural laws, seems to underlie also the *Times*'s strictures on nurses' training and in both cases to spring from an even more basic misogyny: women could not be relied upon to be what men considered womanly.

Thus, the unquestioning submissiveness still thought appropriate for the fully trained female nurse was not recommended to the medical patient, by definition an amateur at his task, or at least not when the patient was imagined to be a middle- or upper-class man. In a leading article on the introductory lectures given in October 1876 at the various London medical schools, the *Times* commented urbanely:

It is sometimes convenient for a doctor to have a patient who does not know too much. Such an one is thought more likely to pay an unquestioning obedience, and is, in a thousand ways, in less danger of being troublesome. But he cannot, on the other hand, render that intelligent co-operation which is often the best assistance the doctor can find, while his very ignorance often brings him needlessly under the doctor's hands, and, at the same time, disposes him to quarrel unreasonably with the remedies provided for him, or with the degree of success which attends them. The public may learn a great deal about the causes of health and of disease without any danger to their reasonable dependence on their medical advisers. There will still remain plenty of trade secrets which can be disclosed only to the initiated.

The degree of initiation appropriate for nurses, however, was far more problematic; it seemed doubtful to male observers as otherwise different from each other as doctors and journalists that they would remain "faithful assistants" if they should attempt, with their new educational opportunities, to "render that intelligent co-operation" which the *Times* advocated for the hypothetical male patient. The newspaper's bland but not unreasonable assumption that "the Medical Profession, like the rest, must put up with a good many recruits below the full mental standard"[13] would not have been shared, or at least admitted, by most medical men; on the contrary, its intellectual reputation was a point on which the profession was defensive, and the development of nursing as a career for middle- and upper-class women looked to many of them dangerously like the creation of a body of infiltrating critics and spies.

In general, the medical profession preferred to regulate itself, not to be observed, questioned, and commented upon by outsiders, and particularly not by women. The *Lancet* was only more outspoken than other journals, not in disagreement, in its consequent efforts to discredit the phenomenon of trained nursing. In January 1877, alluding to three recent cases of accidental poisoning in hospitals, it wrote with evident satisfaction:

> The world has recently seen too great reason to fear that "skilled" nurses, even those engaged at hospitals, are not to be trusted with the administration of duly labeled medi-

cines. If to the contingencies apparently inseparable from feminine folly or feebleness, are to be added such dangers as may accrue to the practice of leaving the drugs in a dispensary at the discretion of hospital servants, we venture to think that the outlook is dismal indeed. . . . We have always felt some misgiving as to the possible effect of training nurses up to a point at which they may be useful to physicians and servants [sic] without going beyond the limits of safety. It is doubtless difficult for a young woman, of no great mental calibre and few attainments, to feel herself credited with quasi-medical powers, without becoming possessed of an ambition to use them. . . . The only safeground [sic] against this new peril is to give hospital sisters and nurses—call them what we may—distinctly to understand that they are personal attendants on the sick, nothing more, and to lock away beyond their reach every particle of medicine. . . . These women, . . . for the most part, possess just enough information to be dangerous.[14]

The editors made no comment when they printed a letter of rebuttal from "A Trained Hospital Nurse" which pointed out that in two of the three cases alluded to the nurses involved were, far from being trained, illiterate, and that the third also lacked all formal training. Instead, they returned to the subject on the more elevated plane of theory in a later issue, when the topic of women doctors gave them an opportunity to clarify their views on the fundamental differences between the sexes: "In the economy of nature . . . the ministry of woman is one of help and sympathy. The essential principle, the keynote of her work in the world, is *aid*: to sustain, succour, revive, and even sometimes shelter, man in the struggle and duty of life, is her peculiar function. The moment she affects the first or leading *role* in any vocation she is out of place." If some women became doctors, the *Lancet* warned, others would cease to become nurses, since "it is opposed to the genius of woman's nature to act as helpmate to her own sex." Although men would probably make better nurses anyhow, since "the touch of a man's hand . . . is steadier, more precise, and not less

gentle than that of a woman, . . . man's nature rebels against
the complete surrender of his own judgment and that implicit
obedience in spirit, as well as letter, which are the first essen-
tials of a good nurse." The "craze" for women doctors thus had
to be opposed: it not only discouraged women from becoming
the right sort of nurses but also acted as an "evil influence" on
the wrong sort, giving them exaggerated notions of their skills
and status.[15]

The historical sequence in which women both reformed
nursing and entered the medical profession, however, suggests
a different interpretation from the *Lancet*'s. Elizabeth Blackwell, although an Englishwoman by birth, qualified as a doctor
in the United States in 1849 and succeeded in having her name
placed on the British medical register only ten years later. Elizabeth Garrett Anderson, the first woman to qualify as a doctor
in England itself, received her license to practice from the Society of Apothecaries, which immediately altered its constitution to prevent other women from doing the same, in 1865. Although she was elected to the British Medical Association in
1873 she was for years the only female member. Sophia Jex-
Blake, after an embattled and peripatetic medical education
lasting twelve years, was finally legally entitled to practice in
Great Britain in 1877. The founding of the London School of
Medicine for Women in 1874 was a response by committed
women to their systematic exclusion from existing institutions.
Since the Nightingale School for Nurses had been established at
St. Thomas's Hospital in 1860 and been rapidly joined by other
nurse training schools (as it had been preceded by institutions
like St. John's House), it seems more likely that it was in part
the new visibility of nurses and the possibility of nursing as a
career for educated women that helped to inspire the interest of
some other women in careers as doctors rather than the other
way around—if there was room for one, then there might be
room for both.[16]

The increasing number of trained nurses through the latter
half of the century in itself sufficiently disproves the *Lancet*'s
assertion that if women were allowed to become doctors they
would cease to enter the "secondary" calling. The ominous ob-

servation that "subjects of purely medical and surgical concern are beginning to be included in the 'studies' of the nurse"[17] was not in fact, by 1878, when the editors observed it, an innovation, and their decision to treat it as one merely shows how little ground they were prepared to yield. At the end of 1880, after the nursing crisis at Guy's Hospital had come to its rather shabby end, they were as firm as ever:

> Nursing is not a craft; still less can it be regarded as a profession. There are specialties in cooking and other departments of domestic work; and there may, therefore, be professed cooks, and waiters, and housemaids, and washerwomen, but there ought to be no specialty in nursing, and there can be nothing professional in the work. The sole qualifications required for tending the sick are kindness, gentleness, and quiet cheerfulness of manner, patience, physical strength, a light and dextrous hand, and the sort of intelligence which renders it easy to take in ideas of work quickly, and to pick up ways of doing what has to be done in a cleanly fashion and decently. For the rest the nurse ought to be the servant of the doctor, and should carry out his instructions. . . . The "trained nurse"—that is, the woman trained to nursing as a specialty, is an anomaly. Every scrap of information she possesses beyond the mere routine service of sick-tending is not merely useless but mischievous.[18]

The omnipresence of domestic servants in nineteenth-century England supplied the editors of the *Lancet* with a convenient metaphor for nurses, and the relative scarcity of cooks and housemaids today may make the condition they were used to symbolize seem equally outdated, but in fact domestic life still provides powerful images for the placing of nurses where they will be convenient to doctors. Eva Gamarnikow has analyzed in some detail the operational analogy between doctors, nurses, and patients on the one hand and fathers, mothers, and children on the other and a single example can indicate the effectiveness of such patriarchal metaphors. In a review of M. Jeane Peterson's *The Medical Profession in Mid-Victorian Lon-*

don, Bernard Semmel wrote feelingly of how doctors at the time were "beset by challenges to [their] authority, not only by the lay boards of governors of the great hospitals but even by nurses," a group clearly seen as having no proper challenges to make. For Semmel, the story of these doctors had a happy ending: they "were at last able to become masters of their own house." The force of the metaphor is total; if the hospital were seen as the nurses' house, however, or the patients', or, abandoning metaphor altogether, as no one's house but as an institution in which disparate persons worked together for the common purpose of healing, then a different story would have to be told, and it could not be considered over.[19]

The Victorian domestic metaphor, however, so influential in the period's hospitals, depended for its strength not only on the actual presence of large household establishments in common experience but on the common perception of life itself as divided into public and private spheres—which largely and conveniently corresponded to conventional assumptions about masculine and feminine traits. The hospital, which clearly comprised and required elements of both, was thus a venue in which these spheres and their inhabitants necessarily but confusingly overlapped, and conflict was the result. As Leonore Davidoff has observed of male-female conflicts generally during this period, "The effort of adult middle-class men to maintain their positions of power within the society as a whole and the 'little kingdoms' of their own households" (as doctors often perceived hospitals to be) "seems to have created a kind of 'psychological backlash' within their own personalities. They combined excessive fears of pollution, disloyalty, and disorder from subordinates with a desperate search for a moral order which would help to control all three."[20]

The dogmatism and defensiveness of the language used by the editors of the *Lancet* to express their belief that the duties of nurses were comprised primarily of subservience to the doctor and secondarily of helpfulness to the patient are strongly reminiscent of the same qualities in the demands of King's College Hospital's committee of management for obedience, but the loyalty of Sister Aimee's staff shows them seriously in error in their reading of women's characters. Women could and did form strong bonds to each other in public as well as in private settings, even across the class lines separating nurses from sisters, so that their capacity and willingness to do so in themselves became essential elements in the nursing controversies of the period, as significant as any of the specific arguments over rotation of day and night duty or the content of nurses' training. In general, however, authority and knowledge were the fundamental issues, and the conflicts waged over them were in no case unaffected by the fact that, as an almost exceptionless rule, doctors were men and nurses women.

PART TWO
The Crisis at Guy's Hospital

The climate of anxiety, tension, and prejudice pervasive throughout the 1870s fed the development in 1880 of what was called on all sides the crisis at Guy's Hospital, and it is important still in understanding not only the actual events and the significance with which they were invested by participants and observers alike, but also the subsequent burial of the incident in later histories of the hospital specifically and of nursing generally—in retrospect, the case was seen as an embarrassment. Nevertheless, the crisis warrants detailed attention both for itself and for its implications, which go far beyond its own parties and their period.

In November 1879 the recently appointed treasurer of Guy's Hospital, Edmund Lushington, appointed Miss Margaret Elizabeth Burt to the post of matron at a salary of £150 a year plus board and lodging.[1] The previous treasurer, Thomas Turner, had served in the post for twenty years, and the previous matron, Miss Mary Elizabeth Loag, had held hers for thirty-four. The hospital was as conservative in its practices and policies as these long terms in office suggest. Turner, writing to the *Times* after the issue had become public, denied "the often repeated assertion that reforms in the hospital were urgently needed when the present treasurer entered on his office." On the contrary, Guy's "was in a high state of efficiency at that time, though capable of improvement, as are all human institutions, and, with the cordial assistance of the staff, various improvements had been introduced during my residence at Guy's."[2] Any institution, however, looks very different to someone who has had charge of it for two decades and to another person whose task it is to take over its operations subsequently. To Lushington's eyes, Guy's untrained nurses, distinguished, if at all, by their length of service and loyalty to the individual doctors responsible for the patients in their wards, were one of the last such bodies of women in a major London teaching hospital and an obvious target for improvement.

Although in the heat of the conflict soon to erupt around his action Lushington was frequently referred to as an interloper and outsider he had in fact a long-standing earlier connection with Guy's Hospital: his father, Dr. Stephen Lushington, an eminent lawyer and parliamentarian, had been a governor of the hospital from 1819 until his death in 1873, three years before his son's appointment as treasurer.[3] The *Guy's Hospital Gazette* described him at the time of his death as "the father of the governing body" and noted particularly that "the medical profession is especially indebted to him for his advocacy of the cause of medical education," adding that after Dr. Lushington's "retirement from public life he established, on the confines of his residence at Ockham, [Surrey,] a Home for convalescent patients under the sole management of his daughter."[4] Edmund Lushington, therefore, had known Guy's intimately throughout his entire life. He had also been brought up to value liberalism, innovation, and—specifically—medical education, presumably in some degree for women as well as for men, given his sister's responsible position in the convalescent home. He had also held his office for four years before his decision to appoint Miss Burt matron and undertake the reform of the hospital's nursing services and was thus well prepared to count the cost of his decision beforehand. Far from an outsider, he survived the storm that followed and remained in office until 1896.

Lushington was also a high churchman. His instrument of reform, Miss Burt, who bore an even greater weight of vituperation than Lushington, had received her training at St. John's House, where she was named by Sister Caroline in one of her regular reports as a new associate sister in 1871.[5] She came to Guy's, however, from the Leicester Infirmary, where she had been a notable success as lady-superintendent, as C. H. Marriott, a Leicester surgeon, asserted at the outset of the controversy in a letter to the *British Medical Journal*. Miss Burt's system was, according to Marriott, "in all its main features identical with that which has been so successfully carried out for many years at King's College Hospital." Although Marriott specified that "under this plan, the staff of Leicester Infirmary has lost no power or influence,"[6] the staff at Guy's evidently did not find either his testimony or Miss Burt's training and experience reassuring. Miss Burt did not introduce either St. John's House or any other sisterhood at any time during her tenure at Guy's. Nevertheless, vague but evidently heartfelt fears of religious infiltration and proselytism were constantly introduced into arguments ostensibly dealing with medical responsibility and the care of patients throughout the controversy.

The initial reactions of the *British Medical Journal* to the case were, in the light of what was to come, remarkably temperate. On 29 November 1879 partisanship among the medical students at Guy's was noticed and deplored,[7] and on 6 December Lushington was characterized as "a man of . . . much good sense and knowledge of the world," although he was also invited to retreat from some of the recent changes, such as the rotation of nursing duties, which had upset the staff and perhaps been introduced "somewhat injudiciously [and] abruptly."[8] Even if Lushington had underestimated the amount of opposition his nursing reforms would provoke, however, high-handedness on his part could scarcely have been by itself a sufficient cause for all the trouble that followed. According to Margaret Lonsdale, Miss Burt's boldest public champion, the new matron had been appointed to her post with the assurance

> that she would be supported in any efforts toward reform which she might make, and not the most distant hint was given to her of any likelihood of opposition to such reform on the part of the medical staff. . . . However, the Matron was subjected to every kind of indignity for the simple dis-

charge of her duty. False reports were freely circulated in the hospital concerning her, libels were published about her in the *Guy's Gazette* (a student paper), and printed papers containing abuse of her were given to the patients and distributed among their friends by the old sisters and nurses who remained. Caricatures and squibs of a gross character reached her by every post.[9]

While the issues of *Guy's Gazette* referred to by Lonsdale are no longer to be found in the Wills Library, Guy's Hospital Medical School,[10] she herself achieved some lasting recognition as the former pupil and biographer of Sister Dora of Walsall. Firmly convinced of the necessity of nursing reform and sceptical of the willingness of medical men to accept, much less to facilitate, it, she gave up her own nursing studies to make a contribution to the cause in the form of controversial journalism on the subject.

In an article published in April 1880 in *The Nineteenth Century*, Lonsdale contrasted the traditional character of hospital nursing with the reforms exemplified, though not invented, by Miss Burt, whose case she described as "rather a typical struggle, showing symptoms of a combined and resolute attempt on the part of the medical profession generally to retain the old system of using untrained women as nurses in our hospitals." If such a preference should seem to her readers merely perverse, Lonsdale was easily able to account for it: "the main duty which was inculcated on [the old nurses] from their first acquaintance with hospital work [was] that they must study the character and special requirements and fancies of the particular medical man or surgeon under whom they were placed."[11] Medical men and surgeons, that is, had a strong wish to retain the "servants" the *Lancet* so frequently assured them they deserved and little or no wish to replace them with nurses claiming to be trained or "professed," a term which suggested religious commitment as well as technical expertise.

Most doctors, of course, saw the matter differently. Dr. J. Braxton Hicks, physician-accoucheur and lecturer in midwifery at Guy's, in an article "On Nursing Systems" which appeared in the *British Medical Journal* on 3 January 1880, when the controversy was already embittered but had not yet been publicized outside the walls of the hospital, treated it theoretically, without allusion to specific hospitals. Hick's preference was for "the ward system," in which "the ward is the hospital 'unit'; the sister is its exponent." Hicks used his discussion of this system, in which nurses were permanently attached to particular wards, as the occasion for launching a criticism of nursing by professed religious: "the sister and nurses should be of no narrow religious creed which would urge them to obtrude their opinions unduly, and should be allowed to follow whatever religious usages they like"—though presumably not narrow ones.

The link between organization of the nursing staff and religious expression is left unexplained as Hicks presents his case, but the terms of his attack on what he calls "the central system," the system in fact in use at King's College, used by Miss Burt at Leicester, and recently introduced by her at Guy's, implicitly, even inadvertently, reveal it. Under the central system, which made a matron or lady-superintendent responsible for all the nursing (and, usually, household) services of a hospital, with power to move nurses from ward to ward, a nurse "is less interested in pleasing the medical authorities," a result as bad in Hicks's eyes as it was good in Lonsdale's. If this primary loyalty went without reinforcement, Hicks predicted, nurses would soon band together in opposition to medical wisdom and authority: "The more the arrangements favored the formation of a clique amongst the nursing staff, the more difficult it would be to hear of, or find out the truth of, any errors or complaints."[12] Hicks's assumption, of course, was that only nurses were likely to make errors or be the subject of legitimate complaints, and that only the monitoring power of doctors rather than solidarity or professional standards among nurses themselves could deter incompetence and dishonesty. His apparent liberality in permitting nurses to follow any religion they chose was a part of a generally divisive policy, quite logically coupled with their isolation in fixed wards.

Lonsdale's views on professional competence and responsibility, of course, differed greatly from Hicks's. Although she allowed that the medical profession generally was remarkable for the many "noble, self-sacrificing men among its members," she nevertheless believed and said that some of the profession's support for the old system of untrained nursing in permanently assigned wards came from the alleged fact that "practices and experiments are sometimes indulged in by the medical men, and permitted by them to the members of the medical schools[,] which it is understood had better not be mentioned beyond the walls of the hospital." Insisting on this allegation, Lonsdale continued, "The presence of refined, intelligent women in the wards imposes a kind of moral restraint upon the words and ways of both doctors and students, and I have no hesitation in saying that it is against this, as much as anything else, that they are now, at Guy's Hospital, resisting with all the might they possess."[13]

Rather markedly, even doctors writing in response to Lonsdale chose for the most part not to defend or explain their practices, experiments, or manners but rather to concentrate their fire on the "insubordination" and "espionage" of nurses who complained or questioned. As the March 1874 "Report on the Nursing Arrangements of London Hospitals" in the *British Medical Journal* had itself admitted, "Both nurses and patients more readily obey a lady sister; her presence checks all rough play and coarse joking, and secures general propriety of behavior,"[14] and no one wishes to be seen as defying this admirable goal. Instead, Hicks's animadversions against the central system, which he virtually identified with nursing by a sisterhood, presented such nurses almost as a secret alliance, opposed to the good of the hospital: "the whole nursing staff are more or less closely united . . . obeying the lady-superior, each sister being called by an assumed name, whereby to a certain extent the identity is lost, and the individuality is merged in the general sisterhood."[15] Since it was traditional at Guy's to call nurses by the names of their wards (for example, Sister Clinical) rather than by their own proper names, there was evidently no objection to the loss of the nurses' individuality *per se*—instead, the jeopardized values were loyalty and subordination.

Power and authority were clearly of paramount importance, and the relative merits of ward and central systems of organization were consistently assessed by medical writers in terms of them, never with regard to efficiency or skill. When Miss Burt's defender Dr. Marriott wrote a second time to the *British Medical Journal* to assert that the Leicester Infirmary was indeed properly comparable to Guy's, which had been rather patronizingly questioned, the editors followed his letter with a critical comment quoting an unnamed "shrewd observer" of the nursing at Leicester, particularly Miss Burt's practice of rotating nurses among wards, who reported that this policy "takes away all power of the medical staff over the nurses, and gives that power to the lady superintendent."[16] No further comment seemed necessary to them.

Dr. John E. Neale, a Liverpool physician trained at Westminster Hospital, wrote in support of Dr. Hick's preference for the ward system as specifically and appropriately supportive of young doctors' need to feel superior to someone: "the residents, perhaps holding their first appointments, are made a great deal more *confident in themselves*, knowing that they have *under* them a woman on whom they can most implicitly rely, and whose interests are, as it were, common with their own." Neale's use of the language of dominance and submission continues throughout his essay, which also consistently characterizes all power held by women as necessarily capricious. In the central system, even if the nurses are "every bit as good," the matron or lady-superintendent "not nominally, yet practically, *reigns supreme*. She can shift the nurses about from ward to ward *as her fancy takes her*, and discharge them in the same manner; while, if the medical staff should ever remonstrate, the result is a general snubbing from the governors and the commencement of a series of petty annoyances instigated against them by the matron, who now, after her *victory* . . . is . . . *free from fear* of losing her comfortable home, and may even go so far as to have the *audacity*, when occasion presents, of making open or underhand reports about the medical staff."[17]

The fear of nurses reporting on the actions of the medical

staff to the matron and/or the lay governors of the hospital seems seldom to have been out of doctors' minds, accompanied by a general belief that these reports would certainly be believed and evidently by little thought of refutation as a practical possibility. A letter to the *British Medical Journal* from "A Former House-Surgeon of Guy's" (many of the bitterest complainers against "espionage" preferred to make their accusations anonymously) referred to his experience in "one of our leading provincial infirmaries, where the Nightingale [central] system was considered to be worked to perfection [but where] a most abominable system of espionage was cultivated by the lady superintendent." If readers chose to take this as a reference to Leicester and Miss Burt, there was nothing to stop them. According to the writer, nurses at the unnamed institution reported to the lady-superintendent, who in turn reported to the lay governing body, which supported her, and the medical staff presumably suffered, although the nature and extent of their suffering, like the charges against them, were left unstated. The conclusion, however, was not: a lady-superintendent needed the control of a select committee on which the medical staff was represented because "women are more strong in their likes and dislikes than men are, consequently . . . they are more apt to be swayed by prejudice. . . . they lack the 'judicial mind' which should distinguish the ruler over a large establishment."[18]

That it is now commonly accepted practice for nurses to keep written records of their work, be trained in more than one type of nursing, and move from ward to ward as patients' needs vary should not be allowed to obscure the fact that these things were all seen at first as dangerous innovations, their only important and wholly evil effect being "that the doctors are reduced to a relatively subordinate position."[19] As Katherine Williams observes in her essay "Ideologies of Nursing: Their Meanings and Implications," it was "the claim to be a profession" which destroyed "the traditional relationship between doctors and nurses" and it would seem to be this sense of an endangered, perhaps a doomed, tradition that must lie at the bottom of the medical profession's most chiliastic pronouncements as well as of its tendency to draw the battle lines for the apocalypse across such otherwise unlikely terrain as the question of how nurses were assigned their tasks. Any issue, however, might be vitally symbolic, as an example of Williams's shows: "In the 19th century, when fever was an important criterion of disease, [the thermometer] was used only by the doctor. In the 20th century the thermometer may be used by a nursing auxiliary, for fever has long been supported for doctors by other criteria of illness. . . . The reading of temperature in this context of changing medical knowledge becomes a much less important task and it is then surrendered to other groups."[20]

The relative paucity of medical resources in the nineteenth century, however, made even the thermometer worth fighting over. Like record keeping and the training that would enable a nurse to do more than obey orders, it might signal an outbreak of that independent professional spirit that Florence Nightingale had introduced into the public consciousness and that now seemed everywhere. As Lonsdale coolly asserted, "A doctor is no more necessarily a judge of the details of nursing than a nurse is acquainted with the properties and effects of the administration of certain drugs,"[21] and though most doctors deplored this belief and combated it wherever they found it, the idea would not go away. Few doctors and probably few nurses, however, in the embattled hospitals of this period, can have had the confidence or the security necessary to share Florence Nightingale's ironically philosophic view, stated in her 1863 *Notes on Hospitals*, that their conflicts worked ultimately for the good of their patients. According to Nightingale:

> The collision, often disagreeable, but generally salutary for the care of the sick, between the secular administration and the nursing staff . . . keeps each belligerent party to its duty, and reacts beneficially on the interests of the sick. Even the mutual impertinence, just as often to be heard between nuns and doctors, as between doctors and nurses, is far better for the management of a hospital, and any neglect of the sick is far less likely to pass unnoticed, than where the authority is solely vested in . . . either . . . the

secular male authorities of the hospital . . . or in the spiritual head of the nursing establishment. . . . If we were perfect, no doubt an absolute hierarchy would be the best kind of government for all institutions. But, in our imperfect state of conscience and enlightenment, publicity and collision resulting from publicity are the best guardians of the interests of the sick. A patient is much better cared for in an institution where there is the perpetual rub between doctors and nurses or nuns, between students, matrons, governors, treasurers, and casual visitors: between secular and spiritual authorities . . . than in a hospital under the best governed order in existence, where the chief of that order, be it male or female, is also sole chief of the hospital.[22]

Few participants in these "collisions," though, sought them disinterestedly for the good of their patients—they were themselves too likely to be threatened, even injured, in what occurred. Instead, both sides more or less reluctantly accepted controversy as the necessary consequence of conflicting principles. If few shared Nightingale's evident zest for battle (expressed, indeed, from the sidelines), few on the other hand lacked a good measure of her adherence to principle. Compromise was no one's object, and harmony was a necessary casualty.

Knowledge of the new nursing dispute at Guy's Hospital, significant though it was for medical prestige and the future of medical institutions, only slowly reached the public. Although the early references to it in the *British Medical Journal* as well as later discussions in the *Times* and elsewhere make clear that there was trouble from the moment of Miss Burt's appointment, perhaps initiated even before her arrival,[1] the struggle went on at first without an external audience. Margaret Lonsdale's article in *The Nineteenth Century*, which in fact focused on the wider issues involved more than on the particular case but named Guy's in its title, ended its obscurity. It elicited six different replies from doctors in *The Nineteenth Century* and the *Contemporary Review* and brought action by the Guy's Hospital court of committees, which proposed a resolution condemning it and expressing "unabated confidence in the medical and surgical staff" in the face of Lonsdale's "unwarrantable attack." After a negative vote on this resolution, however, the court passed a much more tempered amendment, formulated by Lushington, "that the Court of Committees disapproved of any publication relating to the management of the affairs of the Hospital by any person attached to the Hospital in any capacity,"[2] thus in effect censuring the medical writers as well as Lonsdale.

The case, however, was already before the public

and could not be called back, nor was Lonsdale by this time in either common sense of the word attached to Guy's Hospital. The granddaughter of a famous bishop of Lichfield and a daughter of a respected canon of the same cathedral, Lonsdale was an independent adult woman with considerable experience of nursing and the politics of nursing. She had trained at first under Sister Dora of Walsall, whose by no means naively un-critical biography (referred to slightingly by the *British Medical Journal* as a "work of imagination")[3] she had recently pub-lished, and also for a short time at Guy's, where a dispute with Dr. Walter Moxon had led to her resignation. She was a strong supporter of Miss Burt in particular and of nursing reform in general, and she seems to have been in the habit of judging doctors on a case-by-case basis, unhindered by any antecedent awe of their profession. She was undoubtedly a churchwoman, but as she pointed out in a reply to her critics she had never belonged, nor had the least desire to belong, to any religious sisterhood. Nevertheless, as she insisted in her rebuttal of her critics, she considered it "impossible to deny that some of the best and most successful efforts in the way of hospital reform have been made by nurses belonging to Sisterhoods of all types," and she now mentioned as an example the All Saints Sisterhood at University College Hospital, which she had not referred to in her first article because of its well-known connection "with an extreme [that is, Ritualist] section of the English Church."[4]

Besides being trained in nursing, independent both financial-ly and by temperament, and a loyal daughter of the Church of England, Margaret Lonsdale was a member of the educated classes—a lady. Nevertheless, and although she strongly sup-ported the training of ladies as nurses, she had no illusions about the diversity of raw material her class presented—she had learned better at Walsall.

> The trials to which lady-pupils subjected Sister Dora were innumerable. Those only who have had to deal with the teaching of women of all ages, from the middle and upper classes, who take to nursing the sick, either because they have had a matrimonial disappointment or because

they cannot get on at home, or think the air of a hospital may agree with their temper, or because they want something to do, or lastly, perhaps the best reason of all, because they honestly want to earn their living, and having little or no education, they do not see their way to maintaining it by any other means, these alone can tell what Sister Dora had to endure.[5]

Doctors who made similar enumerations were apt to conclude that there was no grain in all this chaff, and the *Lancet's* insistence that "nurses must always be *servants*" carried with it a considered judgment that ladies must be altogether excluded from hospital occupations, but Lonsdale reached a different conclusion. Her dismissal of the old Guy's nurses in her initial *Nineteenth Century* article as uneducated "charwomen,"[6] while certainly expressive of class bias, also rested on a recognition that no class was flawless, while her practical experience of hospitals gave her not only a knowledge of the old nurses' deficiencies but some insight as well into the hardships of their lives. "The long hours of work, with no regular interval allowed during the daytime for proper air and exercise, together with the practice of eating their food in the impure air of the wards"[7] all told against the development of either expertise or professional solidarity, let alone moral character.

Lonsdale's references to the specific working conditions endured by Guy's nurses, however, like her assertion that doctors and medical students sometimes sought other ends than the good of their patients, were ignored in her critics' responses to her, although they were corroborated by Miss Burt herself in evidence given to the committee appointed by the governors to look into the dispute. H. C. Cameron, the official twentieth-century historian of Guy's Hospital, describes the charges rather grudgingly: the nurses Miss Burt found at Guy's on her arrival "were untrained; they took money from patients; they spent their evenings off in public houses and in music halls; they did not keep their patients clean, and lastly, they even wore jewellery."[8] In Cameron's judgment, as his overall discussion of the case makes clear, Miss Burt was in fact largely in the right, but this ordering of her charges tends nevertheless to trivialize them, reflecting perhaps the same embarrassment that Cameron himself encountered "when as a young man I addressed questions to my seniors about the great 'Nursing Dispute' which had happened so long ago."[9]

But however quaintly Victorian these issues might be made to appear by later writers eager to minimize them, they of course had no such quality for their participants. As the committee's own report made clear, Miss Burt's changes were structural rather than cosmetic, designed both to concentrate the nurses' work on nursing itself and to create in them a degree of pride in that work and esprit de corps among themselves. They "consisted mainly of a new scale of remuneration, lower in nominal pecuniary amount, but on the whole advantageous to the nurses. Regular and more comfortable meals and better food were provided, cooking by the nurses in the wards was stopped. . . . Every nurse was called upon to enter into an engagement to take her share of night duty when required; and a uniform dress for the several classes was, as a general rule, insisted upon."[10] Despite the frequent assertions by many of the medical staff that Miss Burt's real object was the establishment of a religious sisterhood, the sole religious element in her program was "the regular attendance by nurses and sisters alike at morning and evening prayers, read by herself in the hospital."[11]

The nurses' pay, working conditions, and even training, however, were matters largely ignored by the medical men who wrote articles in response to Lonsdale's. Instead, they continued to stress "espionage," the dangers of religious sisterhoods, and inadequate respect for and submission to not only the doctors at Guy's but the 450 students of the medical school, whose "presence in the wards at all hours" Lonsdale had alleged to be "a hindrance of a serious kind to the nurse's work." Lonsdale's point was that the medical school, which had grown up after the hospital's foundation and not as an original part of the founder's intentions, was properly a subordinate function to the care of patients, but her characterization of the typical student as one who "looks upon [the nurse] as mainly there to answer his questions, to prepare his dressings, to wait upon him while he performs his duties to his patients, and, finally, to set to rights any disorder and to clear away any mess that he may choose to make," only attending to her patients in any time that remained, was clearly a part of her belief in the appropriate independence of nurses and therefore a threat to the hegemony of doctors.[12]

Sir William Gull, consulting physician to Guy's, wrote one of the more conciliatory replies, avowing both agreement with the objective of better nursing and his own long-standing desire to establish a nursing school, but he also expressed disbelief that Lonsdale was entirely responsible for her own article (without suggesting who he thought was) and focused most of his reply on the shortsighted folly of her position: "Oh! Could some kindly demon dispossess these nursing ladies of this too presumptuous spirit, here so naively confessed and defended, there might be, I think, some hope of their success. But to suppose that a nurse can have a knowledge of her work without being taught through the profession, is to betray an almost palpable ignorance of the subject, and of the only way in which the education of nurses can be advanced."[13] Since Lonsdale had not proposed, however, that nurses be educated by some means excluding contact with doctors but instead had been considering the role and responsibilities of fully trained nurses at work in hospitals, not students in nursing schools, Gull's arguments, whatever their independent merit, were beside the point, as were most of the other responses to her article.

Dr. S. O. Habersohn, Guy's senior physician, concentrated on the sisterhood question even in the face of his own initial admission that "the existence of anything of the kind has been denied and strongly repudiated," and he dismissed Lonsdale herself as merely "the mouthpiece of her party," giving "expression to the opinion of those who want to establish a system," a system which must be, in spite of all denials, a religious one.[14] Habersohn's comments make clear that he was unlikely to take Miss Burt's or Lonsdale's word for their intentions: "The staff do not object to lady pupils, so long as they conduct themselves as ladies, not as agents of a system of espionage where truth is held lightly, nor as meddlesome busybodies who interfere with the well-being of the patients." The staff's objections to Miss Burt and her reforms were in themselves, for Habersohn, the evidence that Miss Burt's motives were ulterior and her reforms the establishment of the much-anticipated "system where *the medical men are ignored*."[15]

Alfred G. Henriques, of the London Hospital, denied that his institution exemplified, as Lonsdale had asserted, the "old system"—if this were to be believed, he admitted, contributions would fall off, and the London Hospital depended on the public for £25,000 per annum above its endowment—"but the London Hospital does not recognize the advantages of sisterhoods, and is not desirous of introducing members of any sisterhoods into its wards as nurses."[16] Seymour J. Sharkey, of St. Thomas's Hospital, even went so far as to conclude that "however bad the old system of nursing may have been in many ways, and however uneducated and untrained its members, they, the doctors, and the patients reaped this benefit, that there was no vaunted antagonism, as there now appears to be, between medical treatment and nursing."[17]

In general, doctors preferred harmony to any improvement or attempted improvement which might challenge their authority or uncover matter for scandal. Octavius Sturges, of Westminster Hospital, who admitted that a trained nurse's judgment might well be competent and who saw "no reason why an educated nurse should not make use of her special senses in the same manner as we [doctors] do ourselves," nevertheless found "absolute subordination" essential: "The noncommissioned officer obeys commands of the subaltern which he sees to be not over-wise. The regimental officer, conscious that the whole plan of a campaign is a blunder, is not the less prompt in carrying out its details. Such mode of conduct applies precisely point by point to the care of the sick."[18] What the sick would have thought of this Charge of the Light Brigade policy for their care no one seems to have asked, but it had been from the time of Florence Nightingale's service in the Crimea a principal target of the reforms in nursing. If loyalty to a hospital and its medical staff involved a disservice to the hospital's patients then loyalty was the virtue that would have to be sacrificed, and this fundamental value conflict lies at the root of much of the hostility that periodically broke out in hospitals—at King's College between the sisters of St. John's House and the committee of management, at Guy's between the nursing and medical staffs—during this period.

The exchanges between Lonsdale and Dr. Walter Moxon, which very fully exemplified this conflict, had their origin not in Lonsdale's *Nineteenth Century* article, which Moxon duly though vaguely replied to, but during her period of training at Guy's, which coincided with the early days of Miss Burt's tenure as matron. Moxon, like Lonsdale, deserves some introduction. The son of an inland revenue officer, he had been put to work in an office in his teens but rebelled against the discipline of his apprenticeship and decided to matriculate at the University of London instead, passing the requisite examination and entering as a medical student at Guy's when he was eighteen. He achieved early recognition as a student and then as a pathologist.[19]

Moxon seems to have been a complex man, even in the eyes of his most sympathetic colleagues. Described as "warm-hearted, somewhat impulsive, friendly, hospitable, and generous," he also "delighted in argument, and was always prepared to maintain a thesis, and above all, a paradox, with logic, which few could answer, and wit which fewer could emulate. He rarely failed to conquer but, perhaps, almost as rarely to convince. He was eager to persuade, and hard to be persuaded." This assessment is from the *British Medical Journal*'s obituary following Moxon's suicide by cyanide poisoning in July 1886. According to the same source, Moxon "had not been in robust health for years; he had had several attacks of severe haemophysis, and frequently passed blood with the urine. It is probable that he took a more severe view of the case than others would have done, and looked forward to an incapacitating illness with the most intense dread. He had suffered severely on several occasions from headache, and had also endured much suffering by reason of sleeplessness, for which he had resorted to the use of chloral."[20]

It is uncertain how far back in Moxon's life this history of instability and deterioration extended, although his colleague Samuel Wilks described him as having "a very delicate constitution, which showed signs of breaking even when he was a student, . . . buoyed up by a natural vivacity and an indomitable will," and noted that in 1880, the year of the controversy, "he on two occasions suffered from bleeding from the lungs, and was compelled to go abroad, and rest for a term of three months."[21] Wilks may also be quoted to show the difficulty which even a sincerely admiring colleague had in assessing Moxon's character: " 'Moxon could in no way be summarized as an eminent doctor or distinguished scientist . . . men whose methods of procedure are clear to all. . . . Moxon was not one of these; and, in one sense, might be called superior, for he belonged to a class of persons whose mental processes are beyond analysis; he was essentially a genius.' "[22]

Such, barring the last clause, which she would certainly have disagreed with, was Lonsdale's principal opponent. Her own approach to the conflict at Guy's was not at all "beyond analysis"; instead, it was addressed stubbornly to questions of material fact. Miss Burt, according to Lonsdale in a letter to the *Times*, "discovered patients dying, neglected, and covered with sores; ill-treated children, and inefficient or worse than inefficient nurses in the hospital, and she considered that it was inconsistent with her duty as matron to allow such a state of affairs to continue."[23] Moxon's reply to this letter, like his later response to Lonsdale's article, ignored its specific charges, instead labeling them collectively as falsifications in the service of a high church subversion of English hospitals until, "one by one, all the great charities of this country may be brought to bear to further a religious sentiment which is acceptable only to a small, though aggressive, section of the people."[24]

Lonsdale promptly and with evident irritation replied to this charge that she had told the truth in her statements about the care of patients at Guy's: "I affirm that I, a woman of 33, who has gone through a fair amount of hospital training, saw with my eyes and heard with my ears everything that I stated in that letter, and I am ready to swear to the literal truth of what I then wrote,"[25] and she followed this initial declaration with a fuller letter explaining her previous conflict with Dr. Moxon during her period as a probationer at Guy's. Observing mistreatment of patients in a ward where she was working and Dr. Moxon was the physician in charge and feeling unable to cross the hierarchical gap between herself and the doctor by direct speech, she took the diffident (and ladylike) if circuitous course of describing the circumstances about which she was concerned in a letter to her mother and asking her "to forward this letter to Dr. Moxon, with whom I had a slight personal acquaintance, in the hopes that he, knowing me, and being aware that I could have no object in misrepresenting to him about Guy's Hospital, would privately investigate and take steps to end the abuses in his own department." At that time, she states, contrasting it with the present, "I fully believed that he could not be aware of the existence of these abuses, and I would still willingly believe it if I could."

The situation did not develop in accord with Lonsdale's hopes. Instead of "coming across the court at Guy's" to her residence, Dr. Moxon telegraphed her mother for permission to read the letter to the governors, "without, I need hardly say, giving the least idea of the use he intended to make of it." Instead of, as she put it, "confront[ing] me with my own statements, . . . tak[ing] me into the ward, and, in the presence of the sister, prov[ing] to me by ocular demonstration that my statements were unfounded, and then . . . pursu[ing] the immediate dismissal of a liar like myself," Moxon chose rather to present the charges to the authorities coupled with an immediate and complete denial, without any investigation by himself or anyone else, although "these were not such cases as could be known to all the clinical clerks [that is, medical students with responsibilities in the ward], or to any except the sisters and nurses of the ward, whose interest and whose care it was to keep them from the knowledge of the visiting physician. They were, indeed, grave charges, and I could amply have substantiated them had Dr. Moxon given me the opportunity which he took care never to do."[26]

Since the issue of patient care was at last inescapably before the public Moxon now replied at length, justifying his own procedure and giving his own version of the state of the patients in question. Protesting that he had not had time to see Lonsdale before the governors' meeting and excusing his use of her letter by pointing out that he had read it without giving her name, he proceeded at last to address Lonsdale's specifics:

> One was the case of a poor little girl paralyzed and blind. The letter described her as having been allowed to get into such a state of filth that, among other things, sores were about the neck where her bedgown was tied. The second case was that of a poor jaundiced woman with internal cancer, and the letter described the poor woman as having had bed sores caused by rude and rough treatment.
>
> Now the ward in which these things were said to be is one that is set apart for the most important and interesting cases. It is called the clinical ward. The physicians take charge of this ward in rotation, and while in charge of it they give clinical lectures upon the carefully selected cases that occupy the beds. There are 32 beds, and the right or duty of reporting the cases in them constitutes one of the higher honorary appointments [for medical students] at Guy's. . . . The little blind girl was in this way attentively watched and cared for by an Oxford graduate, an accomplished and high-minded gentleman, who gave the whole of his time to the care of the five patients under his charge. On hearing of the statements made in Mrs. [sic] Lonsdale's letter, this gentleman sent to me during my speech before the Governors a letter of astonishment and denial, which I read to the Governors. The poor woman with jaundice had died the day before the Governors' meeting, and her body was inspected at the time of the meeting. A report made by the officer who conducted the inspection was handed to me while I was speaking. Its purport was to the effect that a most careful examination showed no traces of any bed-sore, either recent or old. I read this report to the Court of Governors and then left the case between the unnamed letter-writer and the responsible officers of the hospital in the hands of the Governors.[27]

Firm as its assertions are, Moxon's letter leaves several questions unanswered. If his motive in concealing Lonsdale's name from the governors was as chivalrous as he implies, how has her signed letter become tainted with the suggestion of deliberate anonymity on her part in his concluding sentence? If Moxon had no time to discuss the charges with Lonsdale before the governors met, when and how did he arrange to receive both the Oxford graduate's letter (Moxon, like some of the advocates of lady-nurses, could make a snobbish appeal when he saw a use for it—most medical students were not university men) and the autopsy report on the body of the "poor jaundiced woman," both delivered so dramatically during the meeting itself? Why did Moxon omit visiting the ward himself and questioning the sister or invite the governors to do so?

It also seems remarkable that a body of medical men as opposed to rotation in nursing duties as was the medical staff at Guy's should so wholeheartedly embrace the same practice when it came to themselves that the ultimate supervision of the ward changed regularly from hand to hand and at the same time was also delegated to a shifting body of medical students, presumably six or seven of them at any one time since each was assigned five patients out of a possible thirty-two. Although the accuracy of Lonsdale's charges is by now impossible to substantiate, her assertion that only the sisters and nurses were in a position to know the full truth is certainly made more likely by the loose structure of their supervision. It also seems unlikely that thirty-two critically ill patients under the care of no more than three nurses would be entirely free of bedsores even without "rough and rude treatment." Overwork and understaffing, coupled with the primarily educational light in which the medical school considered its "interesting cases," might well account both for what outraged Lonsdale and for what moved Moxon to impassioned defense.

In any case Moxon's and Lonsdale's collision in the hospital preceded and doubtless embittered their public exchanges, and Moxon had at least no reason to misunderstand the nature of Lonsdale's charges. Notwithstanding this, he persisted in his reply to her *Nineteenth Century* article in treating what she said not in its own terms but as motivated by an inflexible determination to establish a high church sisterhood, or at the least its individual partisans, as nurses and sisters at Guy's. Accusing Lonsdale of wholesale invention here as he had earlier before the hospital governors, he offered a list of six admirable sisters who had left Guy's under Miss Burt's regime—not by their names but by their class positions, "granddaughter of a baronet, . . . a niece of the late Bishop of Winchester,"[28] a list Lonsdale challenged in her reply to her critics. Two of the six, by her count, had been dismissed for cause, one before Miss Burt came. One was never a sister at all but a temporary appointee who was unsatisfactory (but presumably also dismissed by Miss Burt), and the other three all "removed before the present Treasurer was appointed, and therefore *some years* before Miss Burt came to be Matron of Guy's Hospital."[29] Again, the particulars, mostly because of Dr. Moxon's suppression of names (which in turn is reminiscent of Sir Charles Daubeney), are lost, but even the *Medical Times and Gazette*, critical of Lonsdale though it was, was disappointed in the replies her article received—"They strike us forcibly as being too much on the defensive. . . . No new ground is taken."[30]

The facts alleged in the quarrel between Lonsdale and Moxon were probably stated on both sides with too much partisanship for any fully satisfactory conclusion to emerge from those statements alone, and there was no independent investigation either of Lonsdale's charges or of Moxon's defense. The next phase of the case was to show, however, that even investigations would not necessarily provide answers acceptable all around: unbiased conclusions were not only difficult to draw but perhaps not even invariably sought, nor were unwelcome conclusions easily accepted by those whose interests were threatened.

The Governors' Investigation and the Ingle Case

In July 1880 the Guy's Hospital board of governors issued the report of a committee it had authorized to investigate the dispute over Guy's nursing arrangements; its conclusions were favorable to Miss Burt. In the same month, however, a case occurred in the hospital in which a nurse was charged with manslaughter in the death of a patient. Both events exacerbated rather than resolved the trouble between the medical staff on the one hand and Miss Burt and the treasurer on the other, although the intention of the governors, at least, had certainly been just the opposite.

Initially slow to act, the governors had not begun their investigation until March of 1880, when they held private hearings to receive the evidence of the medical staff. H. C. Cameron, who had access to transcripts of the evidence so obtained, found them anticlimatic, as the governors themselves seem to have done:

> Sir Thomas Acland, for the Governors, cross-examined the Staff with some severity. Dr. Habersohn and Dr. Pavy both proved unsatisfactory witnesses, consuming a great deal of time on matters of little importance. Dr. Moxon, apart from one or two outbursts, was strangely silent, Dr. Pye-Smith precise, constructive, and convincing. Of the surgeons Mr. Davies-Colley clearly made the most impression. Dr. Steele [the su-

perintendent of the hospital] gave his evidence admirably. He laid stress on the point that the nursing arrangements were in a period of transition and that the one system could not be expected to mix with the other without ferment. Nurses trained on the old system were at the moment in equal number with those trained on the new. In a year or two, he thought, they would hear no more of all these difficulties.[1]

It is worth noting that Dr. Habersohn and Dr. Moxon, two of the committee's poorest witnesses, were also two of the most frequent letter writers who kept the case before the public, while the superintendent, Dr. Steele, who considered the reaction to Miss Burt's reforms to be quite out of proportion to their reality, never stated his views outside the hospital. The apparent unanimity of the medical staff's opposition to Miss Burt and all she stood for (whatever they took this to be) thus appeared to the public to be more complete than it actually was, and the collapse of their opposition in October 1880 was probably less surprising to internal observers than it must have been to laypersons following the case in the *Times*.

The committee's report, issued publicly on 24 July after being presented a month earlier to the governors, summarized the results of fourteen days of testimony and investigation. Treasurer Lushington had removed himself from the committee after its third meeting "to leave them entirely free in their enquiries,"[2] but their support of Miss Burt remained strong:

> The committee are satisfied that, in all changes which have been introduced, there had been an honest endeavor to supply properly trained nurses for the hospital, to provide for their comfort and health, and to place them in a position of due subordination to the direction of the medical staff. But frank communication and hearty co-operation between the medical staff and the authorities responsible for the supply of nurses are necessary for the success of this endeavor. . . . The committee are of opinion that there has been an exaggerated estimate of the effect of these changes on the sisters

and the nurses. . . . In about two thirds of the wards there is now no dissatisfaction, and in many there is reason for believing there is considerable improvement. There is no valid reason for believing that in any case is interference with the orders of the medical staff either sanctioned or connived at by the matron. . . . Although the recent excitement and controversy have tended to unsettle the minds of the students, there is no reason to think that the present nursing arrangements put any real hindrance in the way of medical observation, or practice on the part of the students.[3]

The report's conclusion manifests a certain bewilderment with the extraordinary furor over Miss Burt and her reforms. Although, as the committee tactfully though rather vaguely conceded, "needful changes were introduced without sufficient consultation and preparation" and "some details were unduly insisted on," "the Committee [could] not find sufficient justification for the difficulties which [had] existed between the medical staff and the matron almost from the date of her entrance into the hospital, nor [could] they see in the present state of feeling, any just ground for calling upon her to abandon the duties of a post which she did not seek, but which she was specially invited to undertake."[4] The committee did allow that the staff's resentment of Lonsdale's article was understandable, since they saw it as "an attack from within the walls of the Hospital on their professional honour," but they noted that they had found no "evidence that anyone now in the Hospital was responsible . . . or had any knowledge of its contents before it was printed."[5] There were, that is, no grounds for blaming Miss Burt.

The committee concluded its report by recommending improved communications between the medical staff and the governors, but many of the staff preferred to go on communicating with the press. The *British Medical Journal* expressed great dissatisfaction with the report,[6] and Dr. Samuel Wilks, a physician on the staff of Guy's, denounced it in the *Times* as "little more than a defense of Miss Burt and her acts."[7] Disagreeing altogether with the report's conclusions, Wilks insisted that the

"new system of nursing . . . was to make everything subordinate to the new matron, and . . . the best interests of the hospital [to be] overlooked for the benefit of the nurses." This point,
however, since Wilks also claimed that Miss Burt's reforms
tended to "reduce independent, self-reliant and conscientious
women to the position of subordinates and servants,"[8] seems
specious at best. The medical profession consistently sought to
place nurses in just such a position and made no claim to be
doing so for their "benefit." Wilks's real objection thus seems to
be to a more responsible position for nurses, not a weaker one.

The independence and self-reliance of nurses, avowed on all
sides to be central to the dilemma of nursing reform, well represented at one end of the spectrum of opinion by Lonsdale's demand for better training and more responsibility and at the
Lancet's opposite one by its editors' insistence on absolute subordination, now came before the public in concrete form in the
case of Nurse Pleasance Louisa Ingle, charged with manslaughter in the death of a consumptive patient, Louisa Morgan. Indeed, so strong an identification was made at the time between
this specific case and the theoretical issues it could be seen as
embodying that the two were seldom or never, to the considerable disadvantage of clarity and fairness, separately discussed.

The first public mention of the case thus came in a letter
from Dr. Habersohn to the *Times*. Habersohn, one of the doctors who had replied to Lonsdale in the *Nineteenth Century*,
maintained throughout his participation in the crisis that the
development of a religious system was his primary fear, since if
"religious observances" were "the first consideration," the
needs of patients would "come last." "We have no hesitation in
saying," he continued firmly, "that under the new regulations"
(which Habersohn consistently averred were religious) "the
patients have less chance of recovery than before," a remarkable assertion but one he proved to his own satisfaction by citing the Ingle case:

> Our valuable nurses have been replaced in many instances
> by those who are without knowledge; but in others by
> those who consider themselves so highly trained, that they

can act independently of the doctors' directions. The painful death of a patient during the last few days is the best illustration of this kind of nurse. A young married woman, with threatening consumption and tubercular disease, who was apparently doing well, gave the nurse extra trouble accidentally. The nurse, no doubt without intention of injury, but probably for discipline, dragged her to the bathroom, placed her in cold water for 20 minutes, and then, after adding a little warm water, left her there for another hour. The disease was greatly aggravated by this treatment, the patient became prostrate, and did not recover from the shock, but died a few days ago. No comment is needed. The trained nurse carried out her own thoughts and feelings and the unhappy patient suffered.[9]

Needed or not, a good deal of comment ensued, much of it directed at representing Nurse Ingle's action as the necessary outcome of Miss Burt's reforms, even though the prior question of Ingle's responsibility for Morgan's death had not itself been as definitively answered as Habersohn believed. At the inquest Morgan was reported to have been admitted to the hospital for "phthisis or consumption . . . associated with hysterical symptoms." The attending physician, Dr. F. W. Pavy, "had urged the sister from time to time to try whether she could not get this patient up for an hour or two." When, on 5 July, Dr. Pavy found Morgan "in an altogether altered condition," he was told by her in the presence of Nurse Ingle the story of the bath: "The deceased said, 'I could not help it. It is a mistake that anybody is likely to make sometimes,'—by what she said wishing him [Dr. Pavy] to understand, as he believed, that it was an act of punishment," presumably for a soiled bed. Three days later, on 8 July, Morgan died, of "tubercular and inflammatory disease of the brain," a disorder Dr. Pavy attributed to the shock of the bath episode, which was reported somewhat differently by Ingle and the sister in charge of the ward, whose permission to administer the bath Ingle had asked and received.

Ingle, however, seems not to have made a good impression on the jury at the inquest. She did not know the patient's diagnosis but had been, presumably by the ward sister, "led to believe that it was . . . hysteria," a term which does figure in the diagnosis and which to most people at the time had the same connotations it does today of malingering and imaginary illness. A belief that Morgan was merely dramatizing herself might at least account for Ingle's apparent lack of any sympathy for her. She said that she had not "dragged" Morgan to the bath but "supported" her there: "She thought the patient's object was to get carried, and witness found she could walk." She also believed the bath itself lasted not more than forty-five minutes, about half as long as Morgan had alleged. Both assertions, while probably factual, reveal a thorough indifference to Morgan's weakness, and Ingle's manner, along with Pavy's view of the cause of death, was probably influential in the jury's decision to commit her for trial for manslaughter.[10] Since Morgan had died, "hysteria" now seemed an insufficient diagnosis.

The trial, which ended in Ingle's conviction, produced no new information about the bath incident. Ingle, as the defendant, was not allowed to give evidence, and Miss Burt, though present, was not called upon to testify. A new subject of dissension, however, did emerge from it, providing further evidence that the apparent solidarity of Guy's medical staff was in fact not so complete as it was generally claimed to be. Dr. Pavy's evidence was, as might have been expected, consistent with his earlier remarks at the inquest: Morgan's death was due to the shock of the bath operating on an essentially hysterical previous condition. Dr. Pavy had himself recommended "that the patient should be encouraged in every way to walk." Sir William Gull, however, now gave conflicting testimony, which according to Cameron "led Counsel to engage in much argument as to which was the more eminent Physician and which opinion should determine the issue,"[11] a proceeding which no doubt helps to explain the exacerbated tone of their subsequent letters to the *Times*.

In Gull's opinion, "nothing that Nurse Ingle had done, however unwise and unfortunate, had caused the death." As the autopsy proved, Morgan was in fact suffering not from "hysteria" but from tubercular meningitis, a condition which might have been recognized sooner but had not been and which was itself quite sufficient to account for her death. According to Cameron, whose view of the evidence is medically informed, "Gull and not Pavy was clearly in the right,"[12] but this was not clear to the jury, who sent Ingle to prison, and evidently did not strike the *Times* either as of much importance in comparison to the question of authority over nurses.

According to the *Times*, "It seems hardly too much to assume" (in spite of Gull's evidence, based on the clinical report on Morgan's body, that the death had not been caused by the bath) "that this unfortunate case is a not unnatural result of the controversy about nursing by which the little world of Guy's Hospital has so long been agitated." The *Times*'s argument is circuitous, but its general idea seems to be that the new system's tendency to "centralization, by which the authority of the 'sister' of the ward over the nurses is diminished, and the latter are encouraged to appeal from the sister to the matron"[13] somehow inspired Ingle to act independently, even though the evidence at the inquest clearly stated that she had secured the sister's permission for the bath, acting neither independently nor under the advice of Miss Burt. Lonsdale's comment on the case, however, was the only one which questioned the sister's role in the events, a fact which she herself convincingly explained: "To every trained nurse it appears that the sister of the ward must be held gravely responsible in that, according to her own showing, she gave permission to a nurse to put a consumptive patient into a bath without first asking for medical orders. . . . The Sister in question is an old Guy's sister, but she is a well-trained and efficient nurse. I worked under her for some time. I have reason to know that she is this. But surely even this very grave charge cannot in any fairness be laid to the matron's account? Nor can it be charged upon the 'new system,' since it happened in a ward under the care of an old sister."[14] Ingle herself was indeed a recently hired trained nurse,[15] not, as even Cameron misstated the fact, "one of the new lady-pupils appointed by Miss Burt,"[16] but a case in which a nurse's conduct, perhaps even to the point of fatality, was open to criticism was too much of a windfall for Miss Burt's opponents to let pass, even if its particulars did not really support their claims, perhaps especially if they suggested, as this case's did, that the old system's familiar understandings between physicians and loyal ward sisters could lead to careless medicine and a need for convenient scapegoats.

For Guy's medical staff and their supporters, the important point, as the *Times*'s leader written after the case was decided clearly stated, was "the claim of physicians and surgeons to exercise supreme control over the nursing. . . . It is the physician or surgeon, not the nurse, who is held to have succeeded or failed in the management of a case. . . . Without control over every detail of treatment, physicians and surgeons who have attained eminence or who seek it by legitimate means, will not undertake the responsibilities of their calling."[17]

Considering that Ingle had gone to jail for her failure while Pavy not only escaped any responsibility for his faulty diagnosis and general suggestions to the ward sister for Morgan's treatment but also felt free to complain of Sir William Gull's "unwarrantable aspersions upon my professional competency,"[18] this seems a perverse conclusion, but if eminence is a profession's chief end it is understandable: "competency" under such circumstances will be tested more by reputation than results, and reputation was a consideration seldom out of the minds of late Victorian medical men. Not only Dr. Pavy but Dr. Moxon[19] wrote to the *Times* attacking Gull for his evidence—their demand that their colleague, out of professional solidarity, retract a piece of sworn legal testimony demonstrates in its very irrationality the intensity of their concern.

Not everyone was convinced. On 11 August the Guy's Hospital court of committees, a weekly business committee whose minutes are primarily concerned with leases, deeds, and rents, passed a resolution more in keeping with the facts than most public commentary on the case had been, a resolution also expressive of the increasing frustration of Guy's administrators with its medical staff: "Resolved, that this Court having considered the report of the case of the Queen v. Ingle, and having regard to the remarks on the management of the Hospital contained in it, which are in many instances calculated to mislead, is satisfied that had the regulations laid down for nursing in the Hospital been properly carried out the unfortunate occurrence would not have taken place, and it believes that the nursing arrangements which have been lately revised will fully meet all difficulties, provided free and friendly co-operation be re-established between all persons concerned in carrying on the work of the Hospital."[20]

The day-to-day work of Guy's Hospital continued to be done, but there was no growth in friendly cooperation. In September, prompted by Dr. William T. Iliff, the St. Saviour's Board of Guardians, a charitable body located in the same parish as Guy's, addressed an unsolicited memorial of what purported to be concern to the governors in the public columns of the *Times*. Alleging that they had "heard with regret" of the controversy, which they attributed to the "determination of the [governors] to make the [medical staff] subordinate to the nurses," they expressed a continuing hope "that the governors would yet see their way clear to modify the present system, so that all concerned might work more harmoniously."[1]

The extreme inaccuracy of this formulation, its origin outside the hospital (Dr. Iliff had a private practice in South London and had no formal connection with Guy's), and its publication in the *Times* seem to have combined to goad the governors into decisive action. They began by replying—also in the *Times*—sharply, specifically, and at length. In the first place, the issue was not the business of the St. Saviour's Board of Guardians; in the second, no proposal to subordinate doctors to nurses had ever been suggested, let alone implemented. Their statement summarized yet again the history of Miss Burt's appointment and the substance of her changes in existing regulations, stressing their consistent purpose of improving actual nursing;

> The rules were intended to secure more punctual attendance in the wards, to remove all excuse for doing any work in the wards not directly beneficial to the patients, to distribute the work . . . so as to secure a thorough training of probationers of whatever social rank, to diminish the menial work of the trained nurses, which had been a serious hindrance to their proper duties in former times. . . . No new measures have been introduced which in any way diminish the authority of the head nurse [sister] or encourage nurses to act on their own responsibility, irrespective of the medical authorities; nor is there any justification for the suggestion that the orders of any one of the medical staff with respect to a patient under his care are not, and have not been, implicitly and immediately obeyed.

The governors pointed out their own "careful and protracted inquiry" and its failure either to unearth real weaknesses in the nursing or to satisfy the staff, which persisted in producing only "exaggerated inferences from a few particular occurrences, repeated over and over again, or general denunciations of the abstract principle of some supposed new system alleged to have been introduced." Now, although they had "endeavoured to comply with the wishes of the medical staff as to the allocation or retention of nurses in particular posts, and as to the regulation of their hours, so as to suit the convenience of the physicians and surgeons," their expectations of either goodwill or good sense were clearly waning:

> these and other overtures of conciliation have been met by renewed acts of opposition either in the form of collective protests or of attacks in the public journals, and by peremptory demands for the dismissal (as the only condition of peace) of an officer [Miss Burt] whose intentions and acts the staff, in the opinion of the Governors, wholly misapprehend, who earnestly desires their assistance and advice, but with whom they refuse to communicate, notwithstanding repeated entreaties to meet her personally.

> The Governors are not aware of any obnoxious rules or arrangements which need modification, but if at any time such need should arise, the weekly committee [sometimes called the taking-in committee] appointed by the Governors will give the medical staff, through the representatives they have been requested to select, the opportunity for making their requirements known.
>
> If, however, the medical staff do not attend, still more, if they refuse to attend the weekly committee, it is not possible for the Governors to deal with the requirements which the medical staff do not afford them the obvious means of dealing with.

The governors closed their statement with the specific warning that as they were appointed under Act of Parliament to administer Guy's Hospital it might become their "painful duty" to take action against the staff if "struggles for power" continued to subvert the institution's charitable ends.[2]

The next move was obviously up to the staff, who made it with such clumsiness that the governors easily retained the upper hand. A letter on behalf of the entire medical staff but signed by Dr. Habersohn and John Cooper Forster as senior physician and senior surgeon was addressed to the president of the governors, Henry Hucks Gibbs, protesting the governors' statement. As Gibbs read this letter, it "imputed to the Governors 'that they are continuing a system which they know to be mischievous,' "[3] an allegation of deliberate mismanagement. According to the *Times*, Dr. Habersohn and Mr. Cooper Forster declined to withdraw their language "unreservedly," and the court of governors thereupon asked them to resign, issuing a printed ultimatum to the members of the staff at large:

> That it is essential for the well-being of the Hospital that the Medical Staff and the Nursing Department should work in harmony.
>
> That the Medical Staff having persisted in ignoring the Matron appointed by the Court and confirmed in her appointment after patient investigation of all complaints against her, while she, on her part, is willing to submit

herself obediently to the orders of the Physicians and Surgeons in all matters directly affecting the treatment of any patient, this Court finds that it is the attitude of the Medical Staff which impedes the harmonious working of the Hospital.

That Dr. Habersohn and Mr. Forster, having made themselves responsible for a circular in which they refuse the means offered by the Court for bringing all complaints before it [that is, places for representatives of the medical staff on the taking-in committee] and impute to the Governors that they knowingly persist in a mischievous system, are hereby required to resign the posts which they hold in the Hospital.[4]

After almost a year of increasingly inflamed and abusive controversy the real crisis had come, putting both the resolution and the solidarity of the medical staff to the test. Almost at once, both collapsed. The staff withdrew their letter and agreed as well to begin to send representatives to the weekly taking-in committee as the governors had been proposing for some time; in return, the governors withdrew their requests for Habersohn's and Cooper Forster's resignations.

In this moment of chagrin, the *British Medical Journal* acknowledged for the first time that the controversy had perhaps been conducted in a manner "not altogether creditable to either party," although the faults of Guy's medical staff were merely "pardonable irritation, incomplete harmony, and excessive letter-writing" in an "irritating style," scarcely comparable to the "lamentable want of judgment, faults of temper and discretion on the part of the treasurer" or the "painful inefficiency" they attributed to Miss Burt. The editors were nevertheless disappointed in the collapse of the staff's resistance: "Until the last moment, the staff maintained an absolute, defiant, and irreconcilable attitude, from which it might have been supposed that they had thoroughly calculated the chances . . . and that they were prepared to brave the all-powerful wrath of this irresponsible board, which holds them entirely in its grasp. . . . At the critical moment, they have not been able to find unanimity in their own body, nor have they been able to justify the language which they used." By the withdrawal of their letter the staff had acknowledged the right of the governors "to dictate to them the terms on which they shall meet the matron." Nevertheless, the editors clearly still hoped for Miss Burt's removal in the future, when the medical staff would have improved its tactics: "If it should [then] be found on any occasion that the matron is not capable of carry-ing out the new system of nursing, or that this method of nurs-ing ultimately proves to be incompatible with what the medi-cal officers consider to be for the welfare of the patients, it must surely be possible, in the course of future experience, to pro-duce a calm, deliberate and convincing statement of facts, which both sides will agree shall form the basis for general action."[5]

The editors of the *Medical Times and Gazette* also now ac-knowledged that "the mode in which this controversy has been carried on" had been regrettable, but they laid the blame for this on Lonsdale:

> [although t]here has been far too much heat and temper displayed upon both sides . . . we cannot shut our eyes to the fact that this unfortunate frame of mind was first en-gendered by the girlish nonsense gravely submitted to the public by Miss Lonsdale, and silently . . . acquiesced in by the lay authorities at Guy's. We say, girlish nonsense, for such it was to us, and to all instructed medical practioners and students; but it did not seem so to the outer world, which is only too apt to believe the worst of the most be-neficent profession that has ever existed. For this reason, men, much against their will, were driven to defend them-selves against accusations which had their foundation in the morbid fancy of a silly young woman of overweening vanity, and eagerly seeking notoriety.[6]

Why this necessary act of self-defense had to be carried out both intemperately and incompetently—and with a marked disregard for Lonsdale's actual charges—and why the public persisted in distrusting such an altruistic body as the medical profession were not among the questions raised, much less answered.

The *Times*, devoid now of the sympathy it had formerly expressed for the nurses and sisters of St. John's House in their quarrel with the committee of management at King's College Hospital, adopted the position so frequently reiterated in contemporary medical journals, "that nursing is merely one of the means of care, like the administration of medicines or the performance of operations" and that therefore it was a derogation of the dignity of Guy's medical staff that they should be asked or expected to "confer, or co-operate, or what not" with their own tools. This "unassailable" principle, however, "the medical staff have thrown away . . . by injudicious letter-writing; and they now have no choice but to accept, for a time, the false position in which they have placed themselves."[7]

However, only a short period of penance seems to have been envisaged, and in fact hostilities did not cease. The *British Medical Journal* even resorted to printing misleading student gossip to keep feelings kindled: "The *Guy's Hospital Gazette* says the medical wards are still in a somewhat chaotic condition, in consequence of the closing of so many beds. By the removal of patients from Stephen to Bright, ten male beds have been closed. It is rumoured that Samaritan Ward is to be wholly or partially shut up. The nursing difficulty will be altogether obviated when the hospital is emptied of patients. 'They made a desert and they called it peace.' "[8] As the editors probably knew, however, the closing of some beds at Guy's was due not to the nursing crisis but to the decline in Guy's revenues from its endowments, as a reading of the minute book of the court of committees makes clear. Guy's owned considerable rural property, and a severe agricultural depression was forcing the hospital to reduce its rents. The governors in fact attempted to keep the wards open by means of a subscription among themselves and the staff, but their appeal failed to receive sufficient funds.[9]

At the end of the current term of the medical school Dr. Habersohn and Mr. Cooper Forster resubmitted their resignations, and this also served to keep the case alive, even though responses to their action varied. The editors of the *Medical*

Times and Gazette treated the resignations as the justified result of the governors' brusqueness in dealing with the staff's original letter and its withdrawal ("No word of regret at the misunderstanding, no feeling of sympathy, nor a word of thanks for duty well done, was there expressed. . . . It was not possible that men possessed of a shadow of self-respect could tamely submit to such treatment"),[10] while the editors of the *British Medical Journal* preferred to regard it as important but not critical, commenting that the two men were near retirement, had not concerted with their colleagues, and were acting personally. Numerous of the magazine's correspondents, however, saw Habersohn and Cooper Forster as martyrs, and "Two Senior Students," as they signed their letter, proposed a threat of mass resignation: if the governors were given a two- or three-week ultimatum there would be no possibility of their securing a new staff and "the upshot must be the reinstatement of the entire staff and the former regime. . . . Certainly, if any harm came to the patients, the Treasurer alone would be responsible for it."[11] This indifference to the fate of the patients so long as the blame for it could be laid at someone else's door was perhaps not universally shared, or perhaps the *Medical Times and Gazette's* belief that at the time of the staff's letter to the governors "there was a scheme cut and dry, ready for the contingency of the resignation of the whole Staff," with replacements ready in the wings, "and that the list of names . . . included some of whom better things might have been expected,"[12] awakened a certain prudence among the medical staff.

It was indeed true, however, that the governors neither felt nor expressed any regret at Habersohn's and Cooper Forster's resignations. At their 16 February 1881 meeting, Sir Trevor Lawrence proposed a resolution expressing the governors' "grateful acknowledgment of the long period of active, faithful, and valuable service they have devoted to the work and to the interests of Guy's Hospital," but after a discussion not summarized in the minutes he withdrew his motion, and no other was substituted for it.[13]

In spite of the still general support of the profession as a whole for their embattled brothers at Guy's, critical voices were beginning to be heard as well. A writer signing himself "A Metropolitan House Surgeon" gave good reasons for concluding Habersohn and Cooper Forster to be mistaken in their resignations:

> The fact is, they adopted this course at a time when there was no quarrel between the staff and the treasurer and governors, and when the staff generally had adopted certain terms, including the appointment of a taking-in committee, which they had agreed to try, and which is believed to be working well. [These resignations were] only another example of isolated, . . . irritated, and unwise action. Had they remained at their posts . . . there is good reason to believe that, at the close of their professional connection with the hospital . . . the majority of the governors would have elected them as governors . . . and thus the first step would have been taken towards infusing a medical element into the court of governors, and this by a natural and unstrained process.[14]

If this had indeed been the governors' intention, their disinclination to flatter the two men further by formally regretting their resignation is understandable; they were at least an equally offended party.

In January 1881 the *British Medical Journal* published a letter from Dr. Wilks maintaining that the staff continued to be unanimous in its opinions and had furthermore "been occupying much time and holding numerous meetings, in the pursuit of the cause" (unspecified, but presumably the restoration of the old system of nursing) "which we have always had in view," a vague but still ominous formulation of the current state of affairs, and another from Dr. Hicks saying that all accounts of the events at Guy's were thus far imperfect: "When the time has arrived, of which you must leave us the right of judging, we shall make a statement respecting the dispute, and our position."[15] No such account, however, ever appeared, and the controversy was alluded to as briefly as possible when, in 1892, Wilks himself published his *A Biographical History of Guy's Hospital*. Wilks necessarily referred to Habersohn's and

Cooper Forster's resignations in his biographical essays on the two men; in his comment on the *Guy's Hospital Gazette* he remarked that "it has now existed for twenty years, having had a short interval of abolition during the time of the 'nursing dispute,' when it became a party organ."[16] A party organ seems an unlikely thing to find in a situation of complete unanimity, but by 1892 Wilks probably saw things rather differently than he had in 1881. His placing "nursing dispute" in quotation marks suggests a desire to minimize, if not to deny, the great controversy of a decade ago.

In March 1881, however, when feelings were still evidently sore, the publication of new nursing regulations allowed all sides to claim victory, and the daily business of the hospital was enabled to go on somewhat more smoothly, neither reformed out of recognition nor altogether as before. According to the *British Medical Journal*, which naturally interpreted the situation as favorably as possible, the issue was "virtually ended"by the new regulations, which "have been submitted to and approved by the medical officers, and which concede all for which they have contended." This was to say the least an overstatement:

> Under the new regulations, the nurses are placed under the direction of the medical officers. Each ward is to be nursed by a lady-nurse with two head-nurses under her; and, as under the old regime, these nurses are, as far as possible, to be considered attached to the ward and retained there. . . . Again, the matron loses her new title of superintendent. . . . Finally, the probationer nurses, after serving for one year, will need to have certificates of efficiency signed by the medical officers as well as by the matron. Thus all three main points at issue are virtually decided in favor of the medical men, as common sense should have dictated at an earlier period.[17]

Miss Burt's title had been given by everyone on all sides as "matron" throughout the dispute, so it is difficult to see any concession on this point. What surely mattered more was the fact that she and Lushington remained in their posts, and the

Medical Times and Gazette made clear that the new regulations in fact conceded a good deal less than the *British Medical Journal* claimed and perhaps believed. Nurses and sisters continued to be "responsible to the Treasurer, [Hospital] Superintendent, and Matron" rather than to the taking-in committee and its newly appointed but still voteless medical members; and the medical officers in charge of the wards in which probationers were trained were to be asked to give their opinion on the candidates, not to make unappealable decisions on their fitness. At the end of a probationer's year of training (a period twice as long or more as the training given before Miss Burt's arrival) she was examined on "her fitness for nurse's duties by the matron and one or more of the Medical Staff," a provision that makes clear that cooperation rather than dominance was still the principle on which the governors wished the hospital to operate.[18]

Miss Burt's continued power was evidenced rather surprisingly in August 1881 by the governors' request that Sister Clinical, the subject of Lonsdale's frustrated appeal to Dr. Moxon over a year before, "resign her position because," the *British Medical Journal* commented sourly, "she is unable to work with the matron."[19] As the minutes of the court of committees show, Sister Clinical's resistance to the new regime was indeed what led to her removal. On 3 August the monthly taking-in committee requested the treasurer to ask for her resignation in exchange for a gratuity of a year's salary, and on 10 August Lushington reported to the court of committees that he had "informed her that in consequence of her imperious and offensive conduct towards several of the Nurses that have been from time to time sent to her ward" she was requested to leave; the governors, despite the agricultural depression, made no objection to thus securing peace at the cost of £50. Although the medical members of the taking-in committee protested, they remained firm, and Sister Clinical had to go, though with her gratuity and a testimonial raised on her behalf besides.[20]

The *British Medical Journal* was no more willing than Dr. Moxon had been before to believe that there were any flaws in Sister Clinical's work and attributed her dismissal entirely to the "blind and unlimited" confidence of the governors in the "unamiable and unworkable character" of Miss Burt,[21] but it is noteworthy that, despite the testimonial, there was now no letter-writing campaign or leaking of internal dissension to the newspapers. Someone perhaps had learned something, whether factually about Sister Clinical's management of her ward or politically about tactics and the relative importance of particular issues.

On the other hand, Guy's continued occasionally to receive unwelcome publicity. In July 1882 the hospital was censured by a coroner's jury for allowing students to give information on death certificates without senior staff seeing the bodies,[22] and in October of the same year an inquest was held on the body of a cabman who had been refused admission to Guy's after a fall and died half an hour after his return home of "concussion of the brain with effusion,"[23] according to the surgeon (not associated with Guy's) called in by the cabman's wife. The jury, in returning a verdict of accidental death, added their opinion that "a want of common feeling had been shown on the part of some person at Guy's Hospital."[24] This judgment was obviously much less severe than that imposed upon Nurse Ingle but it was quite enough to arouse considerable resentment on the part of the house surgeon who had sent the man home: in his opinion death was due to "other causes totally irrespective of the trivial bruise to his face," which was rather differently described in the *Times*'s account (but not in the *British Medical Journal*'s) as contusions causing bleeding both from above the left eye and from the nose. According to the house surgeon, death had been "no doubt engendered by habitual drunkenness," a judgment which led him to comment more generally that "the number of drunk and incapable people brought to the hospital surgery at midnight has of late much increased, and the necessity of finding accomodation [*sic*] for more serious accidents, precludes the possibility of admitting alcoholic cases."[25] It seems, in fact, that making moral judgments on the worthiness of charity patients, as in the case of Morgan's "hysteria," remained an accepted medical prerogative, sometimes embarrassing in its consequences but only actually punishable if committed by a nurse.

In December 1882 Guy's medical staff's long-standing wish came true: Miss Burt resigned from the hospital—not under pressure from her critics but on the occasion of her marriage. The *Times*'s brief notice of this event—"The British Medical Journal understands, on good authority, that the matron of Guy's Hospital, whose changes in the nursing arrangements brought about so much controversy between the medical staff and the governors, is about to retire from her post"[26]—seems to imply that she was leaving in disgrace, but the *British Medical Journal*'s own account is surprisingly friendly:

> much and severe as was the opposition which she raised during the early part of her career at Guy's, and serious as were the troubles to which she and her somewhat injudicious supporters gave rise, she carries with her into her retirement the good wishes of nearly all those with whom she has been most intimately brought into contact, and the assurance of their appreciation of the rectitude of her motives. In many respects Miss Burt has rendered a service to the nursing of Guy's Hospital, which she has latterly improved. With somewhat more suavity and discretion, she would certainly have encountered much less opposition. To some extent she was the victim of circumstances, acting under a system of tentative lay dictation. . . . On the whole it may be said that the storm which Miss Burt raised, like most similar disturbances, has had in the end a salutary effect, and Guy's Hospital is all the better for her short but stormy passage through it.[27]

This is a remarkably altered assessment of Miss Burt's reforms, her motives, and her character, and the fact that such consistent critics as the editors of the *British Medical Journal* had so far reversed their earlier stand—although they stopped short of saying so overtly and adopted a minimizing and jocular tone for the tacit admission they had at last arrived at making—is in itself striking evidence of what Miss Burt had achieved. Probably the most significant fact about her reforms, however, is that they were sufficiently well established to survive her departure. Cameron, writing in 1954, described them as in place with little change in his own day, concluding that this fact supported the governors' position in the controversy: "the Matron . . . has taken her place as a third party in the partnership between the Governing Body and the Medical Staff. The nursing care of the patients, upon which everything else depends, as well as the control of the Nurses' Training School, is entrusted to her. It was a momentous and beneficent change."[28]

The value of these changes, however, was far from immediately recognized—as the *British Medical Journal's* comments on the resolution of the crisis proved, they were scarcely even admitted to have occurred. When a fund-raising campaign was launched on behalf of Guy's in December 1886 (its revenues from its endowment of agricultural property having continued to be inadequate), the *Times* took the occasion to demand a reorganization of the hospital's administration to assure that any new funds would be well spent. Their argument was that Guy's at the time had a body of sixty governors,

> largely composed of public men whose time is fully occupied in other duties. There is a committee, consisting of twenty-one of these governors, and having nominal control over the institution; but the practical outcome of the system is to leave the management absolutely in the hands of a high official called the Treasurer, who, being human, is not necessarily gifted with the sound discretion and the varied knowledge which alone could render his personal government in all respects advantageous and satisfactory. Only a few years ago, the then Treasurer, rashly set himself to revolutionize the system of nursing in the hospital, with the result that for some days there was danger of the retirement of the whole of the medical and surgical staff, and that the preposterous alterations intended were not finally set aside until the services of some of the senior physicians and surgeons had been lost to the institution.

The average reader of the *Times* would scarcely infer from these remarks either that the superintendent, Dr. Steele, existed, that Lushington was in fact still treasurer of Guy's Hospital and would remain so for another decade, or that Miss Burt's "preposterous reforms" were still in place, but all were true, and even the *Times* did not allow these conditions to prevent their support of the hospital's appeal for funds. "The hospitals of London are public institutions absolutely necessary to the welfare of the community," the editors instead concluded, in spite of their earlier warnings. "They not only provide skillful treatment for the poor in sickness or accident, but they are essential to the conduct of medical education, and without them there could be no doctors, and no advancement of medical science."[29] The argument seems more interested than charitable, but the effect for Guy's was the same.

At the great inaugural meeting held at the Mansion House to launch the appeal, the nursing at Guy's was a topic frequently recurred to, but no longer as a problem of any degree. The bishop of Rochester in an exhortatory speech asserted that "a hospital was not only a place of pain, it was a place of joy. If there existed a place on earth where there were angels in human form earning happiness and giving happiness it was a hospital. He was alluding, of course, to the sisters and nurses. (Hear, hear.)" On a somewhat more mundane but more practically significant level, Leopold de Rothschild commented that Sir William Gull's daughter was now a nurse at Guy's, and Lushington read to the company a letter from Gull, who was in bed with a cold, which related that during his recent attendance on the Prince of Wales he had observed that "notwithstanding all that was done in the Prince's sick room, he was not better nursed or better cared for than any poor patient in Guy's Hospital. (Cheers.)" Dr. Pavy now added his voice to testify "that the greatest unanimity now existed between the medical and the nursing staff at Guy's Hospital. He said that at the present time the nursing staff was everything that could be desired."[30] No one undertook to explain how all this harmony had come about, but from the fact of its existence there were no dissenting voices.

PART THREE

St. John's House and Its Council

Sister Aimee, Joseph Lister,
        and Dr. Hayes

No matter what assertions of unanimity and harmony Guy's, in the enthusiasm of a fund-raising campaign, felt able to make at this point, the medical
establishment generally continued to regard lady-
nurses with suspicion and to raise the familiar issues
of subordination and authority whenever some new
controversy developed. The dispute which arose in
1882 and 1883 between the St. John's House sisterhood
and King's College Hospital was no exception to this
pattern; it was also, however, a quarrel over personalities, publicly over that of Sister Aimee alone, and
it is therefore necessary also to bear in mind the distinctions between men and women that typically reinforced personality conflicts in Victorian institutional politics.

Sister Aimee's personality had already been
brought up as a serious grievance in the dispute of
1874, just as Miss Burt's "unamiable and unworkable
character"[1] had later been held to be responsible for
the trouble at Guy's, and a belief that women's personalities automatically unfitted them for positions
of authority was widely accepted. As an anonymous
letter writer in the *British Medical Journal* put it early in the controversy at Guy's: "None but those who
have lived in a large institution where the matron has
much power, and is determined to make her presence
felt, can understand how utterly unfitted for governing a woman is. The tyranny, injustice, and I might

almost say, cruelty to her unfortunate subordinates, are such as can only be inflicted by a woman on another of her sex."[2] As the *Lancet* explained it, "women are naturally of an aspiring nature [*sic*],"[3] inherently dissatisfied with their proper place and role, and this perversity warranted a special distrust and scrutiny of any woman exercising or claiming a right or capacity to exercise any degree of judgment or authority. If "feminine folly or feebleness"[4] inevitably impeded or misdirected feminine action, then it was necessary to look no further than the nursing staff to find the cause of trouble in a hospital. Men might theoretically share in original sin, but to affix blame to any individual man, particularly a doctor or a surgeon, seems in practice to have been virtually unthinkable. As W. H. Smith had written to Dr. Beale in 1874 of the King's College committee of management: "I have the strongest reverence for the motives of the ladies who are engaged in this work, and it is quite possible that ignorant and vulgar men may have failed to treat them with the consideration they deserve and that some of them may have the power and the responsibility of government. [Nevertheless, i]t is I think contrary to all experience that such a body should capitulate even if they are in the wrong."[5]

In 1874, however, the hostile members of the committee, although they had resigned rather than capitulated, had been out-maneuvered after failing to make their case, and in 1880 the medical staff at Guy's had found themselves in the even more humiliating position of having indeed to capitulate, withdrawing their letter of complaint, sending representatives to the taking-in committee, and beginning, however reluctantly, to cooperate with Miss Burt. Very few members of the London medical elite can have found the position satisfactory, and it was perhaps inevitable that a new case eventually developed, focusing yet again on the threat apparently posed by a tyrannical nursing sister.

For a time, however, relations between the nursing and medical departments and the lay administrators of King's College Hospital appear to have been genuinely peaceful. The new secretary, Edward M. Forster, was as favorably disposed toward St. John's House as Walrond had been hostile, and he seems to have fairly represented the attitude of the reconstituted committee of management, whose unanimous resolution in praise of the sisters he forwarded to their council on 28 January 1875. The committee expressed its "deep sense of grateful obligation for the kind, ready, and efficient manner, in which the management of the nursing . . . , and the superintendence of the domestic arrangements of the Hospital, have been conducted under circumstances of unusual difficulty and inconvenience, in consequence of the extensive repairs, which it was found necessary to carry out without interrupting the work of the Hospital." They specifically placed "on record their hearty appreciation of the devoted earnestness, with which the Sisters, one and all, have worked for the interests of the Hospital," stressing the sisters' "ready compliance in every particular with the wishes of the Committee."[6]

In a similar resolution forwarded the following year, Sister Aimee was singled out for special praise:

> [the committee] wish likewise to express their warm appreciation and thanks for the unremitting care and attention which the Sister Matron has bestowed on the domestic arrangements of the Hospital, resulting in a very considerable reduction in the expenditure. The Committee feel that they cannot speak too highly of the devoted earnestness with which the Sisters one and all have worked for the good of the Institution, and particularly of their cordial compliance even to the minutest detail with the views and wishes of the Committee. The Committee have the greatest pleasure in placing on record their conviction that the Nursing and Domestic arrangements of the Hospital leaves [sic] nothing to be desired.[7]

Both economy and discipline, the principle subjects of complaint in 1874, were thus seen as being under satisfactory control, and Sister Aimee also, according to Sister Caroline in her regular reports to the council, was well pleased with the committee, speaking "warmly of the kind consideration she received from" them.[8]

In 1877, however, both the sympathetic Forster and Sir William Fergusson, the distinguished surgeon, died, and these deaths created vacancies not only on the hospital staff but in the structure of power relationships between King's College Hospital and St. John's House. Forster was replaced by Edward Almack, later bitterly described by Robert Few, the treasurer of Charing Cross Hospital, a long-time member of the St. John's House council, and an impassioned defender of the sisters in their final quarrel with King's College Hospital and a majority of the council as well, as "*a very young man, and the nephew of the sister-in-law of Mr. Bartle Frere, . . . appointed on the nomination of Mr. Frere.*"[9] Frere, who was honorary treasurer of the St. John's House council, a member of the King's College Hospital committee of management, and a prominent solicitor, was to play an important part in the events of 1883 but seems not to have been very active in the affairs of St. John's House before that time. Nevertheless, Few's charge that Almack's appointment was political and presumably brought about by Frere's influence is to some extent supported by its appearance as an accomplished fact in the committee of management's minutes, unpreceded by any advertisement of the position or review of other candidates only two weeks after Forster's death.[10]

More immediately significant for its impact on the nursing staff, however, was the replacement of Fergusson by the renowned Joseph Lister (1827–1912, created baronet in 1883), who was induced to leave Edinburgh and come to King's College Hospital with a number of special favors: "He demanded that his wards should be separated from all other wards, and that they should not be shared by any other surgeon; then he annoyed nearly everyone in the hospital by insisting on bringing with him from Edinburgh his own house surgeon, three senior students, and a nurse to take charge of his wards."[11] Furthermore, the role of the committee of management in Lister's hiring was extremely passive. They were first ordered by their parent body, the council of King's College, to increase the number of available surgical beds by thirty and then, when this order had been complied with, *told* of Lister's appointment. The committee did not, however, resent either the high-handedness of the governing body or Lister's demands for special treatment. Instead, they resolved unanimously at their meeting of 12 July 1877, two months before Lister's actual arrival, to elect him a member of the committee.[12]

Naturally enough, Lister's requirements and the committee's eager compliance with them did not endear him to his new colleagues: the assumption that underlay them was too obviously, as a sympathetic biographer put it, that "without such assistance it would have been almost impossible to plant his new system in the uncongenial soil which was the best that King's College Hospital was able to offer him."[13] The medical staff of King's College Hospital, however, though none of them matched Lister in sheer celebrity value, were in general a distinguished body of men, known for their research work and eminent in their profession: antisepsis, for instance, Lister's greatest claim to fame, was already practiced at King's College Hospital before his arrival there.[14] They had not, however, brought him among them to civilize them but rather to enhance the status of their hospital, and they seem to have been willing to tolerate a certain amount of humiliation for that desirable end—the more, perhaps, because much of the burden fell more directly onto the nursing staff provided by St. John's House than on themselves.

On 11 October 1877, shortly after Lister's arrival, Sister Aimee wrote to Sister Caroline about the impact of Lister's requirements on the costs of nursing the hospital—as has been demonstrated, a chronic and serious concern—and Sister Caroline passed on the report with her own carefully buttressed opinion: "The Superior has lately seen the Treasurer, Mr. Randolph Robinson, who expressed an opinion that *extra* work at the hospital should not be undertaken at a pecuniary loss to St. John's House."[15] The care of a new thirty-bed surgical ward, however, was not the only charge or expense that Lister's arrival created for the St. John's House staff. On 9 November Sister Aimee wrote again to Sister Caroline, although unfortunately only a part of the letter has survived, pasted into the council's minute book: "I have today been informed by the Secretary that the Operating Theatre which has hitherto (except very occasionally) been used only twice a week, is in future to be in use for operations *every* day. This will necessarily entail on us much additional cleaning as well as a heavy addition to laundry expenses."[16]

Lister's arrival thus created problems for St. John's House which were of no concern at all to Lister himself, much less to his young assistants, as a later letter from one of them, John Stewart, the house surgeon, to one of Lister's early biographers makes plain:

> To us coming from the Royal Infirmary with its simple, kindly, commonsense routine, in which patients' welfare and comfort were the first consideration, this cold machine-like system was intolerable. . . . One afternoon as Lister was about to leave the hospital Dr. Duffin asked him to see a boy in his ward. . . . Lister soon satisfied himself that it was a case of osteomyelitis of the femur and advised immediate operation. While some of us proceeded to get things ready in the operating theatre, I went with others to have the patient removed. . . . When we arrived at the lad's bedside the sister in charge told us we could not be allowed to remove him. Why? Because no patient could be removed without a permit from the Secretary! I pointed out the fact that the Secretary had now left the Hospital and would not be back until 10 a. m. next day, that Dr. Duffin himself and Mr. Lister were now in the theatre waiting for the patient and had decided that immediate operation was the proper treatment. All was of no avail. I lost patience and proceeded to wrap the unconscious boy in his bed-clothes in order to place him on the stretcher. But the sister and nurses adopted so resolute, and, I may say, so menacing an attitude that all of my dressers fled—except Addison, who held the ward door open while I walked out with the patient in my arms, the nurse actually pulling at the bed-clothes in an attempt to *rescue* the patient. I carried him to the operating theatre and he was then our property.[17]

Even if we disregard the likelihood that Stewart's memory over a period of more than forty years may have heightened some details and omitted others, this account can still tell us more than it intends of the St. John's House side of the story. It is important that the secretary, once again, was unavailable when needed—like Walrond, Almack seems to have lived outside the hospital, taking his authority with him when he left at the end of the day. His absence, in fact, probably even more than Lister's request (indirectly relayed through a group of medical students), precipitated Sister Aimee's dilemma (if indeed she is the "sister in charge" referred to by Stewart, who may only have meant the sister in charge of Dr. Duffin's ward). Obedience, and very visible obedience, was one of the most essential elements in the continued tenure of St. John's House at King's College Hospital, and the success of the agreement of 1874 depended largely on the clarity of its chains of command. If members of the medical staff themselves, however, broke those chains when it suited them and furthermore involved students in the resulting anarchy, whom were the sisters and nurses to obey? In a choice between a senior medical student recently arrived from Edinburgh and a contract successfully in effect for more than three years, they not unnaturally chose the latter.

Lister's apologists then and later, however, chose to see St. John's House itself as the source of the rules which sometimes impeded his will at King's College Hospital. As Sir Rickman John Goodlee put it, opting for a familiar cliché, "Sisterhoods became veritable *imperia in imperio*, armed with a code of inflexible rules to which not only patients but medical officers were expected to submit,"[18] a very inaccurate description if it is to be applied to the 1874 contract between St. John's House and King's College Hospital but an accurate reflection of the state of irrational feeling in the medical profession at the time. Stewart's recollections include one other specific anecdote, this one concerning the delayed admission of a patient specially sent to Lister from Edinburgh, when once again a problem arose because of difficulties in finding and notifying the secretary, and it was again the sisters who were held responsible. These two anecdotes, in fact, are repeated fairly consistently throughout Lister's subsequent biographies to exemplify his problems on arriving at King's College Hospital, but they are unsupported by other occurrences, by contemporary documents, or apparently by any other sources than Stewart's letter, written forty years after the events. While they probably in some form occurred, they scarcely warrant the conclusions the biographers tend to draw from them, of which the following is a fair sample:

> The nurses . . . conspired against [Lister]. The hospital was nursed by the St. John's Sisters, a rigid and meticulous Anglican Order, who thought the end-all and be-all of their mission was for the patients to have shining faces, smooth bedclothes, tidy lockers, and to say their prayers often.
>
> They resented the extra work antiseptics gave them, the endless washing of basins and mackintoshes. . . . The repressions, rigidities, self-constituted rules, and general exaltation of what they considered the religious cares of the sick above the material needs of surgical technique rendered them unpleasant and over-bearing colleagues, if not actually dangerous assistants.[19]

Religious bias clearly plays a large part in this colorful misrepresentation, but the presence of misogyny and an unquestioning and—for the doctors—convenient division of both labor and status by sex also should not be overlooked. As Goodlee makes clear, the labor appropriate to nurses was emotional as well as physical: "lack of sympathy and absence of enthusiasm amongst the sisters were unheard of in Lister's previous experience. . . . It created an unpleasant atmosphere in the wards. . . . The success of his new treatment depended largely on the loyal assistance of the nursing staff in carrying out details which it was almost impossible for him personally to supervise. Their indifference or veiled opposition was therefore a source of real danger to his patients—a new danger—which the nurses could not appreciate and which only existed where antiseptic surgery was being practiced."[20]

Since the nurses and sisters of King's College Hospital were already familiar with antiseptic surgery and had for years been demonstrating a high level of concern for their patients, it seems likely that at least to some degree Lister confused the welfare of his patients with deference to himself and his chosen subordinates. Sympathy and enthusiasm he required as strongly as cleanliness and obedience: the demand was an aspect of his identity as an almost Olympian figure, to be adored rather than questioned, an identity also displayed in his opposition to the medical education of women. His behavior in refusing the request of the wife of one of his King's College Hospital colleagues who wished to attend one of his lectures perfectly typifies his complacent inflexibility: " 'He went to the anteroom of the amphitheatre and took the lady's hands between both his and said: I am very sorry, but I have never given lectures to a lot of doctors with a lady present at the same time. I hope you will forgive me, but you will understand.' "[21]

The problems posed by Lister for St. John's House were not accompanied by the charm evidently appropriate to the wife of a colleague. Sister Caroline's report of 15 April 1878 commented with evident discouragement, "The nursing work at King's College Hospital has been very trying during the last six months and the increase of work and pressure on the nursing staff in the *Surgical* Ward on *Sundays,* days which were formerly days of at least partial rest is on all accounts very much to be deplored."[22] Deploring, however, seems to have been all the response possible: the records include no new negotiations over numbers of nurses or conditions of work. Instead, the sisters and nurses absorbed the additional demands upon them as well as they could, with Sister Aimee registering formal complaints with the committee of management—as it was part of her job to do—when particularly difficult situations developed. On 12 December 1878 a letter graphically detailing such a problem was entered in the committee's minutes:

> Gentlemen—I regret to have to bring under your notice some matters which seriously affect the welfare of both patients and Nursing Staff in this Hospital. They also introduce great irregularities into the Wards, besides being, as I believe, practices against which the Committee have from time to time decided. Yesterday, for by no means the first

time, an operation was performed upon a patient in the Fergusson Ward, which began at 1.30 p. m. and lasted till 5 p. m.: the Ward not being free from the Surgical Staff until 5.30, and not cleansed and restored to proper order till long after that hour. I need not point out that there are no proper appliances, nor is there room, in the Wards for Operations, so that when performed there, the whole Ward is turned out, everything in it is misplaced, and a grievous misapplication made of the tables—bedding etc.—Besides this the floors are covered with blood, which is trampled about in all directions; worse still the patients are flurried and frightened, their meals put off or obliged to be given in the midst of all this and the whole routine of the Ward work stopped. What also seems to me very objectionable, all the clinical instruction on the Cases given to the Class must be heard by all the women and girls [that is, female patients, not nurses] in the Ward. Another operation has taken place today (Dec. 11th) in the Craven Ward which caused still greater distress and disquietude to the patients. Several operations have been performed in this Ward lately, although it is not even a Surgical Ward. The mixing up of Surgical and Medical patients in this manner, is an arrangement now too often made, but it entails many evils and imposes too heavy a strain upon the nurses, as well as a great lack of rest and quiet to the patients, there being as a natural consequence little cessation between the visits first of the Physicians, then of the Surgeons or of their several assistants and pupils. The Harass and hindrance in their duties, caused to the staff under my charge, by the above misappropriation of the Wards, is of so severe a nature that I am compelled to seek some remedy at your hands, and I would earnestly request you to be good enough to cause full enquiry to be made into these matters.[23]

According to the committee's minutes, "The Chairman and the Vice Chairman were requested to see Professor Lister on the subject of this letter,"[24] but no further action is recorded; instead, Sister Aimee's letter was ordered expunged and has indeed been crossed out, although it remains perfectly legible. In the future, complaints would be handled more discreetly—but no more responsively.

Publicly, the sisterhood continued to receive the annual congratulations of the hospital's court of governors, relayed to them in exactly the same words in 1880, 1881, and 1882 and duly recorded in their own council's published annual reports: "The Governors desire to renew their grateful acknowledgments for the unvarying zeal, kindness, and devotion which have been evinced in the conduct of the Nursing Department of the Hospital by the Lady Superior, Sisters, and Nurses of St. John's House, as well as for the earnest attention and thorough efficiency with which the Domestic Department of the Hospital has been conducted by the Sister Matron, and that copies of this Resolution be forwarded to the Council of St. John's House, the Lady Superior, and the Sister Matron."[25]

In February 1882 the St. John's House sisters lost yet another friend at the death of their long-term and loyal treasurer, Randolph Robinson, whose health had been failing for some time.[26] Although their council was by definition a supportive body, in practice not all of its members were so well acquainted with the sisters or disposed to see their point of view as Robinson had been. Many as well, like Bartle J. L. Frere, who had succeeded Robinson as treasurer in May 1880, had links to other institutions whose interests might in some circumstances conflict with those of St. John's House; and others—especially, perhaps, such clerical members as the bishop of Lincoln, Christopher Wordsworth, who was married to Frere's sister Susanna—were more committed to the principle of nursing by a sisterhood than to the particular sisters who were engaged to carry it out. This diffusion of loyalties could, in circumstances of less friction, be a positive good, extending the vision of what St. John's House was and what it might become, but in the final conflict between the sisters and King's College Hospital its effect was to divide the council and to leave the sisters themselves unsupported.

In the fall of 1882 both King's College and Charing Cross hospitals were unhealthy places, for the nursing staffs as well as for the patients, a fact that added considerably to the sisters' difficulties in nursing them. On 9 October the council's honorary secretary, George William Bell, addressed a formal letter on behalf of the house committee to Robert Few, his colleague on the council and the treasurer of Charing Cross Hospital as well, on the state of the hospital's drains, which had caused considerable sickness, culminating recently in the death of a lady-pupil. Bell expressed sympathy for the problems this posed to the managing body of the hospital and commented as well that similar problems at King's College Hospital had now been solved by "a thorough course of repair and reconstruction of the drainage."[27] Bell's tone suggests complete cordiality between the officers of St. John's House and those of Charing Cross Hospital, as does Few's immediate reply: "the [hospital] Council have given absolutely unlimited directions to Mr. Thompson the architect to investigate and search out the cause of this sad evil . . . and to do whatever can be done in the matter regardless of expense."[28]

According to Few's pamphlet of a year and a half later, however, matters at King's College Hospital had not been so happily, or at least so completely, settled as Bell had perhaps believed:

> In October 1882, great offense was given to the surgeons of King's by the Sister-Matron remonstrating against the admission of a very offensive *Lock-Hospital* [that is, venereal] *case* in the accident ward at King's. I am told that the patient in the next bed had died of blood-poisoning in consequence, and that others in the ward and both Sisters and nurses were ill from this case.
>
> The Sister-Matron reported this to the house visitors and likewise drew their attention to the large number of phthisis cases then in the Hospital, but the decision of these two visitors was that "*the doctors must do as they thought right in these matters.*"[29]

What remained unclear was the extent of the medical staff's authority in matters affecting not only their own professional decisions but the health and working conditions of the nursing staff. Sister Aimee had not questioned particular diagnoses or treatments, which were without doubt subject to their judgment alone, but an apparently altering admissions policy which affected the health of her own staff and the character of their work, matters on which it was at least necessary that she be informed. Nevertheless, her support among the medical staff was eroding, as Sister Caroline's report of 11 December 1882 makes clear:

> Unfortunately serious and continued illness among both sisters and nurses made the work press very heavily on those who escaped illness. Many of the Sisters suffered. . . . Three nurses died of fever contracted in the wards of King's College Hospital and one lady pupil at Charing X Hospital. . . . It is a sad reflection that [not] until there had been fatal terminations to the attacks of fever in the nursing staff, were any steps taken at either Hospital to make enquiry or seek a remedy, and I am constrained to say that it was by the persevering representations of the Sisters in Charge at both Hospitals of the unhealthy conditions of the wards and of the bedrooms that a thorough inspection was at last made, resulting in the closure of KCH for 3 months, and in very extensive measures at CX Hospital a little later on. Probably the disagreeableness of these importunities will be remembered longer than their valuable results.[30]

Sister Caroline's report continued by detailing the recent visits of delegations from America, Italy, and Germany to study St. John's House's organization and methods, stressing "as a mere matter of justice to her and of interest to the Council" that "it is 'Miss Parry or Sister Aimee' who is clearly asked for and spoken of as the person known to have inaugurated a superior and more conscientious and efficient standard of nursing and to have raised the stamp and tone of the individual nurses." In fact, Sister Caroline's report ends in a full-scale defense of Sister Aimee, not for any specific action but in the context of "an antagonistic, carping spirit, one of constant criticism and inquiry on trivial matters." Clearly, the changes in nursing conditions at King's College which had come about with the deaths of Forster and Robinson, the arrival of Lister, and the appointment of Almack and the reactions to them of the sisters and nurses, formally channeled through the sister-matron, had now brought about a reaction in their turn, one focused not upon the conditions themselves but upon the personality of their leading questioner, Sister Aimee. Sister Caroline tried to put the issue into an institutional perspective:

> As the Sister in Charge of KCH has the control of the nursing and domestic departments—comprising the management of 80 women—as these departments are in thoroughly good working order and have been duly recorded as being so—as the 80 women are contented and orderly and without exaggeration I may add as three fourths at least are warmly attached to the present Sister in Charge and she has the respect of all—I should suggest that it is a pity that slight mistakes should be exaggerated and fomented into offenses, and that there should be any predisposition to consider that she must be always wrong. As a fact things have been represented as being said and done by her, which are not so, and which have been said and done by other sisters, one of whom expresses herself to me that "Sister Aimee is made the butt for all rudeness and fault-finding on the part of the young residents" and that one of them said lately to her "St. John's had had the nursing too long and knew too much." . . . I have thought it best to make the Council aware of this uncomfortable state of things.[31]

The council, of course, with its strong links to King's College Hospital, already knew something of the trouble afoot at the hospital and was inclined, as perhaps Sister Caroline anticipated, to share the convenient tendency to hold Sister Aimee responsible for it. The various frictions attributable to bad drains, contagious cases, overwork, changing conditions, and perhaps to Sister Aimee's uncertain temper as well as to Lister's egotism were of long standing; annoyance existed on both sides and was to some extent accepted as the condition of an imperfect society, though the poor health conditions of the fall of 1882 probably exacerbated it. In November, however, a circumstance arose that converted chronic poor morale and mutual distrust between the nursing and medical staffs into an emergency demanding the taking of sides and some dramatic resolution. Like many hospital crises, the case was an embarrassing one, and the publicity it received was as scant as the authorities were able to keep it. Robert Few, however, after the crisis was over, published not only the main facts of the initial incident but the text of the complaint later to prove central to the controversy:

> a nurse at King's reported to the Sister-Matron a complaint she had received from an out-patient on whom she was in attendance. Thereupon Sister Aimee, having put such complaint into writing and presented it to Mr. Bell, as the Vice Chairman of the Committee of Management of King's [and honorary secretary of the St. John's House council as well], requested his advice. Mr. Bell, having altered three words of the draft, not only sanctioned its presentment, but told her "She would not be loyal to King's if she failed to do so."
>
> The Report was accordingly presented to the Committee by the Sister-Matron and was as follows . . . "That on Nov. 18th the out-patient nurse, in making her report as usual, said '. . . gets worse and worse in the way in which he treats the women. He uses such dreadful language to them, and makes fun to their faces of their ailments. The women feel it very much, and one woman left yesterday, saying she had never been so insulted, that nothing would induce her to come back to the Hospital.' This, the Sister-Matron regrets to say, is a complaint of long standing and frequent occurrence."[32]

The doctor criticized, whose name appeared nowhere in print at the time of the controversy, not even in Few's pamphlet, was Thomas Crawford Hayes, the hospital's assistant obstetric physician. Hayes held the M.A. and M.D. from Trinity College, Dublin, both awarded in 1875, and had been Dr. W. S. Playfair's assistant at King's College Hospital since before the crisis of 1874, at which time Playfair, though not Hayes, had signed the medical staff's remonstrance against the committee of management. Now, however, Playfair and the rest of the medical staff moved quickly in defense of their colleague. While presumably some inquiry was made into the substance of the charge, it was perhaps naturally perceived by Hayes's colleagues as unfounded slander—in fact, since Sister Aimee had conscientiously put it in writing as a formal complaint, as libel. Certainly the charge was by nature a subjective one, of what might be considered only an inappropriate bedside manner, and could furthermore only have been substantiated by the testimony of working-class female outpatients, a trebly inconsiderable, even invisible, group in comparison to a well-known fellow professional. The committee of management's final resolution on the case, which refers to "the evidence brought before them," in fact seems to imply that no additional evidence was actively sought for beyond the confines of the hospital and was made on 7 December, only two weeks after the initial complaint. If the investigation was indeed confined to questioning members of the staff, then the conclusion of the committee— that they were "glad to be able altogether to exonerate Dr. Hayes and to express their regret that the charge should have been made"[33]—is not surprising.

Sister Caroline had been right to warn the council of trouble, and the council responded with a resolution agreeing "that difficulties were arising at King's College Hospital which were likely to prove very serious."[34] Neither the lady superior nor the council, however, referred specifically to the complaint against Dr. Hayes, and they may not have realized at once that this particular grievance required more attention than the rest.

It was agreed that a special meeting of the council should be summoned to discuss relations between the two institutions, but before it could meet the medical board of King's College Hospital passed a resolution urging that "the delicate and responsible functions of the Sister Matron [be] entrusted to someone better fitted to discharge them." The grounds for their recommendation were "that the line of conduct pursued by the Sister Matron has for many years past been adverse to the harmonious working of the Hospital and prejudicial to the interests of the Medical School."[35] The subcommittee of the medical board responsible for this statement was composed of Dr. E. Buchanan Baxter, who had joined the staff after 1874, Dr. John Curnow, who had been on the staff in 1874 but had not signed the remonstrance, and Lister.

Sister Caroline wrote once more to the council. She stated that she had nothing to add to her earlier report but forwarded a letter of support for Sister Aimee from the King's College Hospital sisters, commending it to their "kind and careful consideration, to which I appeal without doubt having myself experienced so much kindness and support during the twelve years passed at St. John's House, and I earnestly ask for your support now for Sister Aimee."[36] The council recorded no direct response to this plea for loyalty. Its minutes for the well-attended special meeting held 27 December 1882 read in their entirety, "Prayers having been read, The report of the Lady Superior, made to the Council on 11th Instant, was read, together with a postscript from the Lady Superior dated this day. After much consideration and discussion the Council adjourned to the 15 January."[37]

The reticence of the council's minutes at the special meeting of 27 December 1882 now became habitual, and since the committee of management practiced a similar discretion a full reconstruction of the actual sequence of events is difficult. The policy was deliberate, stemming from a consistent wish on both sides to avoid controversy, as Bartle Frere himself explained it in a printed letter of 23 February 1883, when the question of Sister Aimee's resignation or dismissal had, despite the council's best efforts, become too inflamed to ignore. Frere's first concern was to justify his own position on both the St. John's House council and the King's College Hospital committee of management, and in the hope of doing so he gave a short history of his relations with both bodies:

> Though I am a member of the committee of management of King's College Hospital, I seldom attend the meetings, except when some matter in which my particular experience is supposed to be useful, and especially when some matter affecting St. John's House is likely to come forward.
>
> I was on the Council of St. John's House before I was elected on the committee of management. I went into that committee at the time when the relations between the hospital and the house were strained to the point of separation. . . .

[Later, a]t the earnest request of the Bishop of Lincoln and another I, on the retirement of Mr. Robinson, undertook the duty of Treasurer of St. John's House, on the assurance that it would be agreeable to the lady superior. At that time my being on the committee of the hospital was not considered an objection to my taking an important office in the house.

Being fully occupied in the duties of a responsible and laborious profession the post of treasurer was not one to be courted by me.

There have been several occasions on which I have been able to assist materially the express object with which I was appointed to sit on the two boards.

Mr. Bell, who has also incurred the displeasure of the ladies, has, more than myself, been most useful by effecting a ready and confidential means of communication between the two bodies, instead of leaving discontent to smoulder till it burst out into formal complaints; and in my opinion in no case has the advantage of such communication been more conspicuous than at the present moment.[1]

The other joint members of the council and the committee of management were George William Bell, the distinguished ophthalmologist William Bowman (knighted on his retirement in the summer of 1883), who had been active in the affairs of St. John's House from its founding, and Dr. Lionel S. Beale, the sisters' aggressive supporter in 1874; in 1883, however, both medical men's loyalty to their professional colleagues stood between them and any sympathy for the sisters' view of their case.

Frere's policy of composing quarrels without written complaints or even, if possible, records seems to have had in fact a very limited value. While informal communications may have flowed smoothly when there was little to communicate, in the exacerbated circumstances of the winter of 1882–83 they created confusion and demonstrably increased ill feeling. Robert Few's account of the charge against Dr. Hayes made clear that Sister Aimee had consulted George William Bell, presumably in his helpful dual role on both the committee and the council, about the propriety of her complaint, and that he had both revised her wording and assured her that it was her distinct duty to pursue the matter formally. Frere's account of the charge follows directly on his praise of Bell but despite his general assertion of Bell's usefulness strikingly omits his contribution on this particular occasion:

> The sister-matron made [in fact, forwarded, with Bell's approval and encouragement] a formal written complaint to the hospital committee against a medical officer. It was a very serious accusation. He came to me in great anger for [legal] advice. I told him I could not advise him [presumably because of the potential conflict of interest, although surely this might also have been seen as a case for Frere's policy of private compromise], but I introduced him to a solicitor of excellent temper and judgment. Had he gone to some solicitors I could name the matter might have led to very serious consequences.
>
> The complaint was referred to a sub-committee of unquestionable fairness, and they so reported on it that the hospital committee could not possibly do otherwise than acquit the physician accused, and express their regret that the complaint had been made. . . . The sister-matron had no doubt the common obligation to notify abuses of which she might have become cognizant, but it was not part of her duty as head of the nursing staff to control the medical staff, so as to relieve her from the common liability to prove the truth of her accusation, and her freedom from ill will. The result of this enquiry seemed to me fraught with danger [evidently of a libel suit], for the accusation had been declared groundless, and it was well-known that there was no want of ill-will.[2]

In fact, there is no evidence that Sister Aimee's charge was investigated at all; that is, that patients were questioned and any sort of overall picture of Dr. Hayes's manner toward them built up. Instead, Hayes was notified, became angry, and threatened legal action, and it was now somehow Sister Aimee who was at fault, responsible both for the proof of the accusa-

tion she had been told it was her duty to make, and for the
further proof that she herself was free from ill will, a standard
no one else was called upon to meet. Even if it is assumed that
Dr. Hayes's manner with female charity patients was intended
to be familiar only to put them at ease and that he was guilty of
no more than insensitivity, a fault his colleagues were well
equipped to overlook, it is evident that Sister Aimee was not to
be allowed the same latitude. Indeed, it seems possible that her
action in the Hayes case, politely admitted by everyone to have
been formally correct, was nevertheless deliberately used as a
device for getting rid of her, the real cause being just what was
denied to be relevant in the case of Dr. Hayes (and in that of
Lister apparently unthinkable)—a manner that gave offense,
but in this case to status-conscious medical men, including students, rather than to ill and impoverished women.

At the 27 December 1882 meeting so briefly recorded in the
council's minute book the bishop of London, John Jackson, who
was also the council's president, "undertook to confer with the
lady superior and sister matron."[3] Jackson, who was known primarily for his administrative skills,[4] did effect an apparent compromise. At the council's next meeting on 15 January 1883 a
letter from Sister Caroline was read offering her resignation and
requesting two months' leave of absence for health reasons.
The council refused to accept the resignation but granted the
leave,[5] which gave them opportunity to place Sister Aimee at
St. John's House as acting superior, an apparently honorific way
of bringing about what was in fact a dismissal. The committee
of management, eager to accept this apparently friction-free
solution to its problem with her, even went so far as to pass a
resolution of praise:

> It was resolved that the Committee, having heard from the
> Council of St. John's House of the intended retirement of
> Sister Aimee from the charge of the Nursing and Domestic
> departments of the Hospital[,] desire to put on record their
> unanimous and cordial appreciation of the zeal and devo-
> tion with which for a period of sixteen years she had dis-
> charged her arduous duties, and of the great skill with
> which she has organized all the nursing of the Institution

and directed its domestic details. The Committee confidently hope that the system which has been so ably set on
foot will lose none of its efficiency in the future, but that it
will be permanently established in the hospital, under the
fostering care of her successor.[6]

Sister Aimee, however, was not satisfied at all by this gentlemanly manipulation. In a letter written two months later,
largely in response to Frere's, she gave her version of her removal from King's College Hospital:

On 16th January the Superior asked me to take her place
for a time, and I, as in duty bound, consented to do so.

I was expressly informed by her that this temporary arrangement was made that she might be able to obtain the
rest she so much needed, thereby to provide breathing time
for the due consideration of the difficulties which had
arisen at the Hospital.

Three days later (on 19th January) a resolution of the
Committee of Management of King's College Hospital was
forwarded to me, which . . . appeared in no way to tally
with the sense of the Council of St. John's House as con-
veyed to me—I felt it to be an unkind, and I venture to
think, an unfair thrust, and one from which I might have
been protected.[7]

Sister Aimee's letter probably exemplifies the sort of behavior
which had made her unpopular with her medical co-workers:
confronted with a contrivance for the comfortable evasion of
the truth, she preferred the latter, and her refusal to go quietly
now superseded and epitomized every previous grievance
against her. It was probably at some time during this period
that Bowman wrote to Lister to apologize for "the annoyance
to which I know you have been so long exposed by the action of
that perverse woman" and to take a share in the blame for the
council's apparent failure to keep "a sufficiently firm hold of its
position within St. John's House."[8] Probably Frere's avowal
"I'm not going to *be beaten by the sisters*" was uttered in the
same context.[9]

On 13 February 1883, Sister Caroline, whose leave can scarcely have afforded her the desired rest, addressed a long letter to the council which only begins with the sisterhood's sense of the injustice of Sister Aimee's treatment. Characterizing Bell's and Frere's communication with the King's College Hospital committee of management as "unauthorized" and "in direct opposition to the intentions of the Council" as she herself had been given to understand them, probably by the diplomatic Bishop Jackson, she drew the conclusion that she had been deliberately "mystified and deluded, for nothing would have induced me to be a voluntary party to the invidious and hurtful treatment to which Sister Aimee was subjected when her [temporary] retirement was converted into a forced dismissal."[10] The episode was of more than transitory significance: "It will be difficult henceforward for the Superior, whoever she may be, to maintain that frank and confidential communication which should exist with those very members whose action has inflicted such an affront on Sister Aimee and on the Sisterhood generally, who had so little consideration for the position in which they placed the Superior, as one who had either entirely misled the Sisters as to the feelings and intentions of the Council or else had been herself made a catspaw of."[11]

If Sister Caroline's tone is any less forthright here than Sister Aimee's the difference is negligible; nevertheless, it became throughout the next several months the practical policy of the council, especially of Frere, to treat the superior with a consistent though rather heavy gallantry while continuing to insist on the personal defects, particularly the offensive manner, of Sister Aimee. The distinction was probably strategic rather than merely eccentric: if an agreement could be reached that Sister Aimee was unacceptably unreasonable then her sacrifice could save St. John's House, whereas if the sisterhood continued to support her then secession was probably unavoidable. Indeed, the menace of a complete breakup of the institution was already proposed in Sister Caroline's letter:

the confidence of the Sisters in their Council is shaken— From the Hospital Committee of K. C. H., they have unfortunately learnt by experience to expect nothing, but from their own Council they do expect and look for such support as shall not leave them when in difficulty, to the mercy of another body[,] whether hostile or not as the case may be. If this fail them then assuredly will the Sisterhood break up, and seek other honest work— The Sisters cannot sacrifice a life and its energies, and in some cases health also to be thrown aside to appease a clamour or whenever the value of their special work is reaped and they are no longer considered necessary to its continuance.

The loss of a united body of upwards of 30 Sisters, gentlewomen by birth and education and all skilled nurses[,] would be a terrible blow to the House and would nearly wreck its prospects of work. . . . Many of the Sisters singly or otherwise would be welcomed by other Sisterhoods, Homes or even Hospitals and there would not fail to meet with the just consideration which they do not receive at King's College Hospital working as Sisters of St. John's House and so precluded from defending themselves.[12]

Noting that she had had considerable difficulty in persuading any sister to take over Sister Aimee's position even on a temporary basis and that none of the sisters at Charing Cross was willing to be transferred to King's College, Sister Caroline now proposed that the proper object of sacrifice was not Sister Aimee but "the connection with K. C. H.," which she viewed as "already lost." Hospital gossip suggested that "other plans have been in embryo for some time past, and those who have mooted them will gain their end sooner or later." A voluntary withdrawal by St. John's House was the course she now proposed.[13]

Bartle Frere's response to the superior's letter was characteristically indirect. Ignoring both the suggestion of withdrawal and the threat to the sisterhood, he continued instead to focus on Sister Aimee. Avowing the propriety and good faith of his and Bell's actions, he now added for good measure the relief felt by the committee of management that this "very painful but necessary change would be made with as little mortification as possible to the Sister-Matron, [and] without any scandal or any breach of the connection with St. John's House"[14]—although he also made it clear that he continued to hold Sister Aimee solely responsible for all difficulties. A new incident supplied him with additional fuel, which he duly added to the fire:

> On 31st January a written complaint was made by Dr. Duffin on a report from the house physician that, on Saturday, the 27th January, he had just seen the first of Dr. Duffin's patients in the Little Twining Ward when at 12:15 p.m. Nurse Coles informed him that the patients' dinners had just come up, and that she must therefore leave him to see to them at once. Dr. Duffin observed as follows:—"At that moment my patients in the small Twining Ward had not yet been visited by the house physician; the consequence of Nurse Coles leaving him was that he was precluded from receiving the morning report on their condition. In two of the cases the report to be expected from the nurse in charge was an important one." He then goes on to describe the serious nature of these two cases, and of the "formidable complications" that had in one arisen during the night, and adds: "On enquiry how it happened that Nurse Coles had been so suddenly removed, Dr. Tompson [the house physician] told me that the Sister-Matron had given him notice that at 12.15, whether he had finished his visit or not, the nurses going round with him would be withdrawn."[15]

If Dr. Tompson had done his morning rounds in the morning, of course, as might have been expected of a young man concerned with the welfare of his patients, some of them "serious cases," not one who had just seen his first patient at noon, the problem would not have arisen, but his superior, Dr. Duffin, accepted the report of his subordinate and forwarded it, just as Sister Aimee had done in the case of Dr. Hayes. Dr. Duffin, however, was not held responsible for ill will in doing so, any more than Frere found that to be a part of his own motive in bringing the matter up to Sister Caroline. What happened instead was that, on behalf of the committee of management, Sir

Richard Wilbraham interviewed Sister Aimee. According to Wilbraham, "the sister matron . . . at once admitted her error, and stated that she was going away then and there, and she promised not to come back." Only with this assurance and the "urgent entreaty" of Wilbraham was the committee held back from further action on Duffin's complaint.[16]

Not only was Sister Aimee held without investigation to be guilty of an incontestably fatal error (her confession of guilt, if it is not greatly exaggerated, is easily attributable to the stresses of her situation) but Frere represents the committee as virtually magnanimous to her. Describing himself as one of Sister Aimee's "most sincere well-wishers," he went on to describe her as "much misapprehend[ing] her position": "I was astonished to find at a meeting of the committee of the hospital at which the medical staff were fully represented, how almost everyone had some instance to relate of affronts administered, a written order sent back torn up, disrespectful messages sent by underlings, nurses withdrawn inopportunely without explanation, a feeling that a system of espionage on the treatment and conduct of the medical officers was in constant operation, restrictions imposed on the necessary intercourse between the medical men and their patients and the nurses."[17]

Even if Sister Aimee is allowed the fullest possible amount of human fallibility she can scarcely have generated single-handedly such a situation as Frere describes. Certainly she had been herself bedeviled by "disrespectful messages sent by underlings," and the medical student who told another sister that St. John's House "knew too much" may be taken to represent the mutuality of any "espionage" under way in the hospital. Nevertheless, Frere's assessment of all the blame to Sister Aimee alone and a condition of total irresponsibility to the medical staff was firm, and he clearly felt no qualms in asserting "how impossible it must be for a body of men of any independence and position to act with a subordinate body, such as the nursing staff must be," directed by so insubordinate a figure as Sister Aimee. Frere's fundamental principle, in fact, was that "nursing work . . . , though so essential and honourable, is clearly supplementary and subordinate [to] the independent and eminent men with whom rests the principal responsibility of an hospital";[18] that is, that female nurses must be not only subordinate in medical decision making but submissive in social behavior to the high-status medical men who staffed the hospitals in which they worked. He never spelled out but clearly accepted the extension of this deference to medical students as well, in spite of their youth, inexperience, and notorious rudeness, and he nowhere mentioned patients save as pawns in the medical power struggle in which he had already chosen his side. It is not surprising that a meeting of the committee of management "at which the medical staff were fully represented" seemed to him to furnish all the evidence he might need, or that he generally ignored the representations of the sisters in their letters; the differences in his availability to the two groups and in his attention to what they said was compatible with these assumptions, which were also the premises on which he undertook what he saw as the defense of St. John's House.

It is hardly surprising that the sisterhood failed either to share Frere's convictions or to see his application of them as just. In their view, "the oldest and most loyal worker of all the Sisters" had been in effect "chosen out to exemplify the uncertainty of our tenure, and to show that length of service, devotion to the Sick Poor, and the highest rectitude, avail nothing." Sister Aimee had had less notice than a domestic servant, instead being "hunted from her post as though guilty of some great misdemeanour." They saw neither advantage to themselves nor minimal justice in Frere's policy of diplomatic informal agreements, asking instead if Sister Aimee's "hurried removal from KCH was an authorized act" and if they might be "supplied with a copy of the Resolution or Minute passed to that effect, and with some explanation of the reasons for such unprecedented action." Failing such a response, which of course could not be forthcoming, the sisters concluded that they could "not but feel that our Council . . . will fail to command our confidence, will condone an unconstitutional act, and offer an affront to the whole Sisterhood." They bluntly stated as their goals the "retirement of [those] members [of the council] who have kept bad faith with the Sisterhood and have proved themselves indifferent if not inimical to our interest"—in this context, clearly Frere and Bell—and beyond that the reformation of the council to end what they considered to be its domination by King's College Hospital.[19]

Sister Aimee's previously cited letter specifically disputed Frere's version of her departure—"I was not aware that I had in any way given [Sir Richard Wilbraham] to understand that I had resigned my post . . . nor had I any idea that I was leaving the Hospital not to return"[20]—but went on to offer assurances of the constructive nature of her intentions. She was not, as Frere had accused her of doing, fomenting resistance within the sisterhood but instead had "aided my substitute, as far as I could in the performance of duties so new to her." Further, if the connection between St. John's House and King's College Hospital should be continued, she pledged herself to "encourage any Sister who may be appointed to succeed me, to accept the post, and without considering the past, I will assist both her and the Superior, as far as may lie in my power, in the carrying on of the work, which I have so much at heart."[21]

It seems unlikely that all of the members of the council were equally satisfied by this letter (almost certainly Frere was not), but the majority chose to accept it at face value and to record a further resolution of praise, seizing what must have seemed an unanticipated last chance at apparent harmony. Expressing their appreciation of the motives dictating Sister Aimee's letter, they went on to state their "strong sense of the energy and ability and especially the untiring devotion to duty, under very difficult circumstances, which she [had] shewn during the sixteen years she [had] held the post." They professed to sympathize "with her regret at leaving a work, the main success of which is owing to her," and to look forward to receiving her continued services.[22]

The date of this resolution was 12 March 1883. On 14 March the medical board of King's College Hospital, having succeeded in the first phase of its drive to secure a larger place for itself in the management of the hospital, appointed a subcommittee to consider the nursing services in general "and to formulate a series of suggestions to be submitted to their Colleagues who are also members of the Committee of Management."[23] The St. John's House council's policy of cooperation and concession had in fact, as the sisters had warned, weakened their own independent position, and clearly the medical staff knew it.

On 4 April, the committee of management passed and forwarded to the St. John's House council two resolutions. The first alleged that "the future harmonious working of the arrangement between St John's House and this Hospital cannot be secured without freedom from all authority and interference, direct or indirect, within the Hospital of the Lady who has so long filled the office of Sister Matron—and they regret to find that, notwithstanding the pledges which she has so often given, that Lady still continues frequently to visit the Hospital contrary to the well understood wishes of the Committee." This was bad enough, though it at least kept Sister Aimee to the fore as a scapegoat for the council's troubles. The second resolution, however, was addressed more generally to the sisterhood and to the council which governed it and was implicitly threatening: "That the Committee take this opportunity of re-affirming and requesting the Council of St. John's House, to recognize for themselves, and to inform the [acting] Sister in charge of the Hospital thereof, that it is absolutely essential that the Medical Staff of the Hospital be alone responsible for the Medical and Surgical charge and treatment of the Patients within its walls, and that their directions in all matters of Diet, Nursing, Ventilation of the Wards, and of the general treatment of the patients [traditionally all matters left largely to the nurses], must be implicitly obeyed."[24]

It was now obvious not only to interested participants but to anyone who could read that the hospital's medical board and committee of management were in agreement not only to expel Sister Aimee but to deny the independent professional competence of the St. John's House sisters and nurses as well, and respect for their masculine peers on the council in no way deterred them from pursuing their goal of an unshared authority over the institution. The word itself became something of a fetish, as a 28 June letter from Almack twitting the council on its failure to prevent Sister Aimee from making further visits to the hospital, "to the great inconvenience and discomfort of the Authorities of the Hospital, and to the great weakening of the authority of the Committee," makes clear.[25] Certainly the sisters themselves parted with it reluctantly, as Sister Aimee's persistent visits to the hospital attest, and the harried council erected another barricade for itself by shifting most of its responsibilities to the smaller house committee, whose minutes now recorded most of the correspondence in the case.

The hostility of "the Authorities of the Hospital" to the sisterhood was even pettily exemplified by the deliberate omission of their name from the hospital's annual report. As she was now acting superior, it fell to Sister Aimee to write on 7 May to Edward Almack to enquire "why the entry of 'Superintendent of Nursing Lady Superior of St. John's House' had been omitted in the report of King's College Hospital for 1882." The reply she received ten days later she was certainly fully justified in considering malicious: "Dear Madam, I regret that some delay has unavoidably occurred in acknowledging your letter. . . . In reply to your enquiry, I beg to inform you that the Annual Report was prepared with great care and every part of it was considered and approved by the Hospital Committee. I must beg leave to assure you that nothing could be further from the thoughts and intentions of the Committee or of any member of it, than to cause any offense to yourself."[26] In other, plainer words, the omission was intentional, and the hollowness of the disavowal of insult—once again insistently aimed at Sister Aimee alone rather than, as would have been obviously more appropriate, at the superior or the sisterhood—seems as deliberate as the absence of any apology or explanation for the slight.

Under such circumstances of constant criticism and conflict it is hardly surprising that the display of harmony mustered for the annual festival in aid of King's College Hospital, though presided over by the Prince of Wales, failed to have any significant soothing effect. The prince's toast praised the hospital's service to patients and its medical school, then added: "Moreover, the hospital was connected with an excellent training school for nurses. He would not go into any disputed points in speaking on this subject, but he felt sure that in these days

everybody knew that, however eminent and valuable the experience and scientific knowledge of the medical men might be,
unless there were properly trained nurses it was difficult for the
medical men to carry out their duties."[27] Some of the hear,
hears that according to the *Times* greeted this part of the
prince's toast—Almack's, Lister's, Bowman's, and Hayes's, for
instance, as of course no women were present—must have been
qualified at least by a strongly combative sense of what constituted proper training. Certainly no reconciliation with St.
John's House followed.

When the council met on 11 June 1883 it faced a long and unpleasant agenda, but its most significant piece of business was undoubtedly the acceptance of Sister Caroline's resignation, a step it had been trying to avoid since January. The lady superior offered to remain at her post for a transitional period of three months, to which the council, determined to be the ones to convey a favor, added an additional month's leave of absence.[1] In fact, the separation of the sisters from the institution whose name they bore would be completed by 18 August after further deterioration of relations, but for the time being the preservation of appearances still seemed important.

Next, Dr. Hayes made a last appearance in the council's minutes with a letter requesting a copy of "a paper, in which somewhat injurious statements respecting my character appear, written by . . . the late Sister Matron,"[2] but the council declined to furnish the paper, no copy of which is to be found in the archives relating to the case, suggesting that its existence may merely have been a hospital rumor, and Hayes did not push his now less threateningly stated grievance. At the same time, uncomfortably balancing Haye's letter in the council's incoming mail, was one from Major General J. E. T. Nicolls, Sister Aimee's brother-in-law, who asked, as the sisters had done earlier, for a clear statement of the process by which Sister Aimee's removal had been effected, and then went on to warn the council of what they were already belatedly beginning to recognize, the full extent of the sisterhood's disaffection. Not only was there, as Nicolls warned, a "strong personal feeling" for Sister Aimee herself; there was besides "a very much stronger feeling on the part of the Sisters as regards their own position, as brought home to them by Sister Aimee's case, which feeling would not be set aside, were Sister Aimee to disappear from the scene."[3]

The council did not record its answer to Nicolls's letter, although Bell wrote one which was later referred to by Sister Aimee. Meanwhile, the report from Sister Aimee herself (still acting superior) read at the same meeting included a letter from Sister Isabel, acting sister-matron at King's College Hospital, on behalf of the sisters there which reported far different conditions from those it had been hoped Sister Aimee's retirement would create:

> I must beg to repeat what we have often said before[,] that we cannot see our way to continuing the training of our nurses here, and that we, the Sisters of King's College Hospital[,] beg you as acting Superior, to give us other work, elsewhere. We have, none of us, any wish to leave St. John's House—on the contrary are most anxious to go on with the work which we undertook when we became Sisters—but the conditions have altered so much here, there appears to be a great deal of jealousy and interference on the part of the medical staff, the feeling seeming to increase rather than diminish, making our work both trying and distasteful. We should really be glad if you could find other work for us, if the Council does not see the advisability of withdrawing from the nursing of the hospital.[4]

Bartle Frere, in his 23 February letter, had anticipated the possibility of the resignation of some or all of the sisters, but he had refused to be intimidated—"I may remind my brother Councillors that something like this [that is, the secession of Sister Mary Jones and seven other sisters in 1868] has happened before, and that St. John's House survived it"—and had gone on to insist upon the priority of the council's rule and of its contract with King's College Hospital:

> I consider the connection with King's College Hospital of great importance to St. John's House as a school for our sisters and nurses, particularly in one very essential point, the experience in dealing with medical men, who cannot be expected [unlike sisters, apparently] to be all of them perfect. . . . I am by no means of opinion that our principles are at fault, though our practice must be amended; and I think if our present ladies, after knowing the facts and considering the position, refuse to accept the decision of the council, supposing it should be that the ladies are in the wrong, we should allow them to go, and begin again. What has been done once may be repeated; and though we may be thrown a little back, it will be only to go on better by-and-bye.[5]

Now, however, with the anticipated resignations actually upon them, accompanied by the realization that there was no question of their "allowing" them to happen, the council seemed less sure of themselves than Frere had proposed that they should be. At their meeting of 28 June 1883 they received, forwarded by Sister Caroline, a highly critical and specific letter of resignation from the whole body of sisters:

> We can no longer doubt that an attempt is being made to change the conditions under which we have hitherto worked, so that instead of being ruled by an experienced and high-minded woman in all such matters as principles of work and details of nursing, these questions are now referred to a Council of men.
>
> The fact that Sister Aimee's position has been made impossible at King's, and that Sister Isabel has, after four months trial, felt obliged to decline permanently to succeed her, that your [that is, Sister Caroline's] name has been removed from the K. C. H. report, as superintendent of nursing, without any protest being made on the part of the Council; the entire disregard shewn to the representa-

tions of the Superior and Sisterhood; your resignation for
the reason that you can no longer consistently with your
sense of right, carry on the superintendence, make us feel
that the standard of our work is, and will be, lowered. . . .
It is scarcely necessary to tell you what pain this gives us.
It is to us all the breakup of a community in which we are
bound together in strong ties of work and friendship. To
some of us it is the loss of a home that we hoped would
have been for life.[6]

Even facing such a clearly unhappy prospect, however, the
sisters remained firm. Formally asked by the council on what
conditions they would remain, they replied with a businesslike
but radical list of demands that they must certainly have
known would not be met, beginning with the resignation of the
council's present officers, including the entire house committee. In future, furthermore, no more than one member of the
council ought to come from any one hospital nursed by the
sisterhood, and that member should not be of the medical profession or eligible for appointment to the house committee. Instead, the lady superior and the sister-in-charge of the principal
institutions nursed by the sisterhood should be ex-officio members of both the council and the house committee. Returning to
a very old grievance that had never been adequately resolved,
they specified that the superior should be elected by themselves
and her election then approved by the council. For the present,
Sister Caroline was to remain as superior. The nursing of King's
College Hospital was to be given up.[7]

It is unlikely that any part of this set of proposals was seriously considered. As Frere put it in a report to the house committee, "the Sisters declined arbitration" (although as Few
pointed out later, no offer of arbitration was ever actually
made) "and the acceptance of their resignations became inevitable."[8] Alleging that they accepted the sisters' resignations
"with the greatest regret," the council still expressed a "hope
that many of them on calm reflection may find reason to regret
their present course,"[9] but the sisters had had ample time, over
six months, for reflection, and there is no indication that any of

the thirty-five ever considered changing her mind, much less did so. In the crisis St. John's House had now reached, their loyalty to each other, and particularly to Sister Caroline and Sister Aimee, easily triumphed over the sentiments that bound them to their name, their past history as an institution, their comfortable residence in Norfolk Street, Strand, or certainly their council. As voluntary workers, their freedom to resign, however misguided a step the council chose to consider it, was unquestionable. The position of the sisterhood's paid nurses, however, was not nearly so clear.

According to Sister Aimee's report of 12 March, St. John's House then employed 219 nurses, 6 of them receiving pensions. These women were paid employees, working on three-year contracts. Their personal ties were to the sisters, who trained, supervised, and worked beside them, but their legal employers were the council, and a struggle now developed over their loyalties and future employment. The council insisted that the nurses were in effect the property of the institution and saw any defections in their ranks as proof of deliberate subversion on the part of the sisters. The sisters in return denied any intention of taking the nurses away with them but remained necessarily in constant contact with them, unable and probably unwilling to conceal from them their own disaffection or their developing intention to reestablish themselves separately from the council. The nurses thus were faced with a decision rather different from the sisters'. They were not completely free agents since they were under contract to St. John's House, and the fact that they worked for their livings compromised even further their freedom to make purely private ethical decisions.

At the council's 10 July meeting a letter from Edward Almack to William Bowman was read which accused Sister Isabel of soliciting the nursing staff to join the sisters in their resignation. Sister Isabel, however, reported in person to the council "that she had told the nurses that the Sisters were leaving on Sept. 16th and that they (the nurses) must come to some decision; she did not ask the nurses either to go or to stay."[10] In fact, even before the sisters could respond to the council's offer of time to reconsider their resignation the house committee had received from Adeline Howard of the King's College Hospital nursing staff—described indignantly by the sisters as "a nurse of only fifteen months' standing, [acting] without the knowledge, much less the acquiescence, of nurses who have been five, seven, or sixteen years in the hospital"—warning of subversion of the nurses by the sisters, and they had reacted ("with a copy to every member of the nursing staff all over the country")[11] with assurances of continued employment and the text of their resolution accepting the sisters' resignation while denying the substance of the grievance.

According to Howard, Sister Aimee had extravagantly promised that "any nurse who left the Hospital to go with [her] should not lose one penny and that [she] should find employment for them all," also that "the nurses should each have 5 weeks holiday and need only come back to the Hospital to pack up and be off."[12] In the light of Sister Isabel's categorical denial of Howard's accuracy this report seems at the very least to have been grossly overstated, but certainly some sort of letter of resignation was written by at least some of the King's College Hospital nurses and addressed to Sister Caroline, who wrote them in return urging them to remain at their posts, carefully showing Bishop Jackson her own letter to document her position.[13] Sister Caroline's letter, however, while it stated the case fairly, still, as Sister Isabel also reported herself as having done, gave the nurses leave to make individual choices rather than a clear directive what choice to make, and was thus not something the council felt could be left to work on them unaided. Responding to their offer to resign in sympathy with the sisters, Sister Caroline had written:

My dear Nurses,
   I received your letter, which touched me deeply, I do so truly sympathise with you in these troubles. It is true that I am leaving St. John's, and that the Sisters all wish to leave. *But your going would cost you much, and it will not be for your good to break your engagements. I pray you to con-*

sider well before deciding on what you may regret. The expression of your feeling to the Sisters will never be forgotten by us.

Full well I know the difference that losing the Sisters will make to you in your work and in your life. All have been so united, and you have been so loyal and true. It nearly breaks my heart to leave you, and know all this is now nearly ended. Some of you I have known for years, for all of you I have a warm regard—your welfare has been near my heart. I cannot say half what I feel, but remember that I am always your affectionate friend.[14]

Addressing a hastily collected nineteen nurses at the hospital on 12 July, Frere put the council's position forcibly. As he later told the house committee, he "explained the misfortune," expressing the council's regret but also a belief that no real harm to the work of St. John's House had been done. Putting matters more bluntly than he was accustomed to do in his correspondence with Sister Caroline, he reported himself as having said that "though the Sisters had retired they were not St. John's House, that we had the money and the power, and a very influential Body of members." Fourteen of the group—"the loyal ones," as Frere called them—expressed a willingness to remain, and Frere promised them the council's support. In contrast, he "warned the 5 adherents of Sister Aimee that as persons of honour they were bound not to make mischief or to try to seduce others from their duty." At this point another nine nurses were brought in, of whom eight proved "loyal." The exception, who struck even Frere as "a very nice person, . . . said she was the nurse who had been concerned in Dr. Hayes case and she had so strong a regard to the Lady Superior that she should not like to go against her. I told her Dr. Hayes case had nothing to do with it. I asked her whether the Lady Superior had not written to her to reconsider her resignation and advised her to go on: She said she had but she should like to consult her and I begged her to do so. The names of the nurses were all taken down and I desired a separate note to be made of her case."[15]

Between confusion and intimidation, Frere seemed to have

saved the day. He made a very full report of his success to the
house committee at their next meeting and the committee consequently declined for the time being to interview Nurse
Howard, who was waiting in hopes of seeing them after submit-
ting a second letter accusing Sister Aimee of subjecting her to
"gross insult," calling Howard, because of her first letter to the
committee, "untruthful, vile, baseborn, treacherous, mean-
spirited coward and other bad names."[16] Whatever else is
doubtful, Nurse Howard's enmity to Sister Aimee is plain, and
the committee may have doubted her reliability even as she
told them what they were already disposed to hear. Despite the
committee's refusal to talk directly to her, however, the council
wrote to Howard on the same date, sending her a full list of the
names of the King's College Hospital nurses and expressing
their obligation for her "marking those Nurses she can be *certain of*, as remaining loyal to St. John's House," and adding,
"Nurse Howard should please hold herself in readiness to return
to K. C. H. any day."[17] In fact, this questionable instrument
seems to have gone on to make herself indispensable, and on 19
September, after the secession was complete and the council
was fully engaged in its attempt to replace the thirty-five sisters
in such a way that they would scarcely seem to have been
changed, Nurse Howard, with her fifteen months' experience,
was made an "Honorary Associate of St. John's House and . . .
the Associate Cross . . . presented to her in recognition of services rendered to the Institution."[18]

Now that the sisters' departure was certain, Sister Aimee
wrote once more to the council "as a matter of business and
common prudence" requesting an "assurance" from them "that
there is nothing against me with regard to the performance of
my duties . . . during the last sixteen years . . . as I have to
carry out arrangements for future work without loss of time."
The council's preference for equivocation was still a source of
trouble:

> The act which caused the Council to desire my removal
> from the post of Sister-in-Charge at King's College Hospital,
> in response to the pressure brought to bear upon them by the

Medical Board and Committee of that Hospital, and which was the only apparent reason for the Council's taking part against me, has been pronounced by the Council to have been "perfectly justified" in the Resolution passed by them on the 11th June. . . . This justification completely exonerates me from the only specific charge brought against me; but in a recent letter, addressed by the Secretary of the Council to my brother-in-law, General Nicolls, it is stated that I am "one of the Sisters with whom the Council is dissatisfied."

From this and other circumstances it is evident that there is still some complaint against me on the part of the Council. I therefore request that as a matter of simple justice, I may be assured that there is nothing against me, or if there be, that I may be distinctly informed what it is.[19]

The reply which the honorary secretary, George William Bell, immediately sent her was perhaps not very "distinct," but it was sufficiently insulting that it could have been of no assistance to Sister Aimee in applying for other employment. Bell wrote as from the house committee, the smaller and more consistently hostile part of the governing body, rather than from the council as a whole, and began by wondering, since she and the other sisters had now resigned, on what principles she could now "call on the Council to give an explanation of your own act," although that was certainly not what she had asked for. Bell then proceeded to dismiss the complaint against Dr. Hayes as "but a minor incident in the course of events," although he failed to name any others. While no one could deny that Sister Aimee had been justified in "preferring" that complaint, however, "it is impossible nevertheless to relieve you entirely from the consequences of your failure," a comment suggesting that these consequences were somehow natural rather than the actions of men. Bell's sketch of a possible reference for Sister Aimee reinvoked the familiar specter of an authoritarian female: "the Council will no doubt be prepared to assure anyone with whom you may wish to engage in fresh work, that they highly valued your services, that your administrative powers and devotion to your duties are unusually great, and that possibly in a position where you are paramount and your will undisputed, you would do excellent work." If anyone were to ask how the council had come to part with "so efficient a coadjutor," however, Bell would be at no loss for an answer: "I may point to the terms detailing the price at which your services could only be retained. The least consideration must satisfy anyone of ordinary discernment that a lady who could pen or subscribe such a document, is not fitted to work harmoniously with others in such a post as that of Sister Matron in a Hospital."[20]

The document referred to can scarcely be the now negligible complaint against Dr. Hayes (which in any case Bell himself had helped to "pen"), but is probably the sisters' collective statement, made in response to the council's own request, of the conditions on which they would retract their resignation. If so, the implication that Sister Aimee bore a unique responsibility for this document fits the general agreement the Sisters' critics seem to have shared that she should be the scapegoat for the entire body. A letter from Bartle Frere to Sister Caroline on 19 July, in which he even uses some of Bell's exact language, reinforces this reading of the prevailing policy, even as it also shows the council's willingness to go back on their own previous statements when their interests appeared to change:

My Dear Madam,

Notwithstanding our wish to comply as far as possible with what you think convenient I am tempted to urge upon you very seriously whether any good can accrue to St. John's House or the Sisters who have determined to quit it by their remaining on at St. John's House. We have selected a Lady to take your duties temporarily and are in a position to relieve you of work which has become so trying at a day's notice. I am particularly led to this by what occurred at St. John's House on Wednesday. I mentioned to you at the Committee that Sister Aimee had planted herself in the passage in a somewhat excited state watching when the Lady we had appointed there departed. When I

went out she was there still looking very thundery and unpleasant. I was in haste, and only gave her a slight sign of
recognition which she ignored but when dear gentle
W[illiam] Bowman afterwards came out and offered his
hand I am told she burst out with a torrent of invective.
Of course the [House] Committee must not be interfered
with in their business and if Sister Aimee cannot command
her temper she must as long as she is at St. John's keep out
of the way. I am afraid my dear Madam she is too many for
you and is able to control your better judgement, and most
kind and obliging disposition. She is doing herself immense
harm and affording a complete justification to her opponents—I sincerely regret it. In a position of paramount authority[,] though[,] with her energy and ability she would
doubtless do good work and though I should tremble to be
under her, she would have my hearty good wishes. She has
thrown up St. John's House except on conditions of abject
submission[,] the most comical composition that has come
under my notice, she can't communicate with temper or
civility with any officer of St. John's House. What is the
good of her staying. However if she chooses to stay she
must conduct herself with reasonable propriety. She is simply a Sister who has resigned[;] she has no authority no
right to meddle in any way with the business of the Institution and is in this house on sufferance and the Committee
cannot allow her to create difficulties or annoyance.[21]

Frere's anger seems to increase as he writes—his transitions
become abrupt and his punctuation nearly deserts him. Nevertheless, Sister Aimee cannot have interrupted the business of
the institution in any literal sense merely by standing in the
passage, however embarrassing the confrontation with her may
have been, and she was no more at fault for the sisters' terms or
on sufferance in their residence than any other member of the
sisterhood. If she spoke angrily when offered the hand of the
man who had described her to Lister as "that perverse woman"
her behavior is at the very least understandable—despite

Frere's avowals of distress at the harm she was doing her own cause, she knew quite well that the cause was already lost, and she had reason to believe she knew why. Sister Caroline, who certainly understood all of this and more very well, made no reference at all to Sister Aimee in her reply to Frere's letter. Responding instead to the only substantive point made in it, the committee's new wish that the sisters should quit the premises sooner than the date previously agreed upon, she stated that she was prepared to leave on 15 September as already planned, or on the 11th if that were better, and concluded with her own reminder of reality as the sisters saw it: "I have not complained of the work as trying having been accustomed to it for more than twelve years. I have no wish to be relieved at a day's notice."[22]

Although the council had lost the entire body of thirty-five sisters they had at least thus far been fortunate in escaping the embarrassing publicity of 1874, nor had the medical staff of King's College Hospital emulated the "injudicious letter-writing" of their colleagues at Guy's. Now, however, a rumor of what was happening appeared in the *Times*, sent in by an unnamed correspondent clearly sympathetic to the sisters, which asserted that "the whole body of Sisters nursing at King's College Hospital have been obliged to withdraw at three days' notice, it being even stated that the gates have been kept locked with the intention of excluding a lady who for 16 years has laboured with unwearied devotion for the benefit of the hospital and its patients."[23] The exact circumstances of the sisters' departure from the hospital were not recorded by any of the bodies concerned, but a note from Sister Caroline establishes the date as 13 July,[24] just after the council's warning to Nurse Howard to be ready to return to the hospital at a moment's notice, and it seems likely that the abrupt banishment of the sisters was a move made in order to secure the wavering nurses. Furthermore, since the sisters were no longer at work (even though they had been excluded from the hospital, not abandoned it of their own volition), there was now no longer any reason other than their own written agreement for the council to allow them to stay on in Norfolk Street until mid-September, and Frere accordingly, on behalf once more of the house committee, began to press for their departure.

The exchange of letters with Sister Caroline which has just been quoted occurred just a week after the sisters' exclusion from the hospital. Although Sister Caroline had given him no encouragement in this policy, Frere continued to attempt to divide the sisters and to qualify the superficially friendly tone of his letters with an undercurrent of vague threat, reminiscent of the manner he had employed in his meetings with the King's College Hospital nurses. His next letter continued the assiduous assault:

When I spoke of the work as trying I supposed that to act with persons whose conduct unfortunately you do not approve must be so. It is very trying to us to act with a Lady whom we value heartily but whose good opinion we do not enjoy and who feels bound to counteract our nefarious projects. The sooner this is put an end to the better and we will accept your arrangement to leave on the 11th September. I only wish you could stay altogether as I am sure you might if an irrepressible Sister Aimee would employ her energy elsewhere. I may say that as soon as this is over and St. John's on its legs again I shall retire from the Treasurership so if you would like to continue as Principal or Sister you would not experience any disagreeables on my account. There is one point I must draw your attention to. I believe so completely in you that I shall not question anything you may decide upon but I think you ought to consider what I say. I do not consider that the existing Sisters can claim what has been contributed from time to time by the Sisters to the Society or House as their own individual property or been purchased out of the Sisters' fund. The fund itself of course after paying whatever may be rightfully due belongs to the House and this will be matter of account but there must be many things presented or on which the money of the Sisters fund has been spent which ought not to be removed. The existing Sisters cannot be regarded as representing St. John's House and Sisterhood of which they are but members constantly fluctuating and changing. No question on matters of small importance shall be raised with my consent, and I shall contend that entire reliance be placed on your known generosity and deliberate sense of duty as to all matters under your control. I am told that the temperature charts were removed from the Hospital. It is of no consequence only an annoyance[;] it illustrates what I mean. I am certain that when to our sorrow you take your leave no such littleness will be found to embitter what is sad enough without.[25]

Sister Caroline, perhaps skeptical of the trust Frere professed to place in her, had offered at the time of her resignation to supply bills of sale and affidavits proving her ownership of the furniture she proposed to take with her, but the house committee had refused to accept them, asserting that their confidence in her precluded any such necessity.[26] As in the case of Sister Aimee's dismissal, the reluctance of the governing body to document what was happening would cause it in the end greater trouble than it saved, but if its goal was to avoid unpleasantness in the present it succeeded—the furnishings of the Norfolk Street residence became an issue only after the sisters' departure.

In spite of the council's professions of good will, it was becoming steadily clearer not only that real hostility toward the departing sisters existed among them as it did among the medical men with whom Sister Aimee had had her original difficulties, but also that this hostility had spread far beyond the actual parties to the case at hand. As Robert Few, the sisters' most outspoken defender, put it:

I was assured—most accurately, as the results proved— . . . that the whole Medical Press would take up the question on behalf of the profession *against* the Sisters. A very few weeks proved the soundness of this warning. Every medical publication denounced a nursing Sisterhood as an undoubted evil, and of course soon obtained the command of the *Times*, the cry of the latter being, Is a Church Sisterhood possible. That the article in the *Times* was contributed by someone connected with King's is beyond question, as it introduces anecdotal matter which not only is not to be found in the Council's statement of November but was never mentioned at any of our meetings at St. John's.[27]

The final phase of the sisters' tenure at St. John's House and the period of their removal thus came before the public in a way that neither the impact of Lister, the debacle over Dr. Hayes, nor the deterioration of their relations with the council and house committee had, and both sides now had recourse to the press.

The Nursing Sisters of
St. John the Divine

On 1 August 1883 the *Guardian*, a church paper consistently sympathetic to the sisters, reprinted an address originally made by them to the governors and subscribers to St. John's House which strongly criticized the attitude of the council—still more of the house committee—to the sisters themselves. Avowing that "the council list contains many names held in great respect by the public, and which we also respect," the sisters nevertheless insisted that those members who held positions in both the house and the hospital "have naturally, and probably unconsciously, been inclined to . . . the point of view that St. John's House is a mere appendage of King's College Hospital." This belief had been relatively harmless "whilst the desire of those in authority was to work with us," but when this desire no longer existed the sisters soon became aware of "the absolute irresponsible power possessed or claimed by our Council." They now concluded "that they [the council] consider the Sisterhood mere instruments for unreasoningly carrying out the will of the Council, however opposed to its own views,"[1] and that they themselves had no other honorable course but to defy that judgment both in argument and in action.

Bartle Frere immediately replied at length, securing reprints of his own letter, presumably for further distribution. Still insisting on the sole responsibility of Sister Aimee for the condition affairs had now

reached, he was also implicitly critical of the rest of the sisterhood for following her mischievous lead, behavior on their part
that no doubt reinforced his belief in the necessity of women's
being governed by men:

> The cooperation of men with women is recognised
> throughout the Institutes of the Foundation; and without
> in the least detracting from the honour due to women, we
> affirm that the evident success of our institution, and the
> survival of it through the dangers to which it has been ex-
> posed, is due to this happy co-operation.
> This characteristic we are not prepared to surrender.
> The Sisters, misled, we believe, by one masterful spirit,
> who has bewitched them, tell us in their letter of resigna-
> tion that, believing they were to be subject to women only,
> they find they are called on to act with men. Undoubtedly,
> this is the case, and must be. They must act with the
> Council, with the medical men; they cannot learn their
> business or practice it otherwise.
> It was this misconception of her position by the one lady
> who is responsible for the defection of our Sisters, and her
> failure to treat with proper consideration her masculine
> coadjutors which has produced the present inconve-
> nience. . . .
> The high standard of our work . . . will be . . . rendered
> much more acceptable, by being united with due consid-
> eration for the rights and position of those with whom we
> are necessarily associated.
> The most eminent men who form our Council take an
> active interest in their duty and have on this occasion de-
> voted much anxious thought and many valuable hours to
> the present troubles. Among them are men of talent, inde-
> pendence, and knowledge of the world, and good Church-
> men not at all liable to be swayed by me or anyone else, or
> lightly to imperil the holy work they have undertaken. . . .
> Even on the one point on which the Council and the Sis-
> ters have disagreed, not an order has been made, nor even
> threatened, nothing but persuasion has been attempted, to

obtain the compliance of the ladies with the wish of the council for the one act of self-denial which the council, the committee of the hospital, and the medical board of King's College all felt to be necessary.[2]

The one act, of course, was the removal of Sister Aimee, and Frere's denial that any orders had ever been issued is his version of the resignation-into-dismissal maneuver which had antagonized the sisters in the first place. There had never been a time, as Frere rather absurdly put it, when the sisters had expected not to work with men, nor had their proposals for a reformed council and house committee asked that men as such should be stripped of any role in the institution. Subjection, however, they did reject, and only subjection, beginning with the elimination of the "masterful" (that is, insufficiently submissive) Sister Aimee, would have satisfied Frere. Despite his use of the term, cooperation had never been his object, and his language generally is more revealing of his contempt than of anything else. He seems to have been able to represent the sisters themselves only in ludicrous and demeaning terms, as in his casual suggestion that they were "bewitched." His only concern now for these women whom he professed to honor was that they should vacate the premises in Norfolk Street as soon as possible:

> As the Sisters [having been banned from the hospital] have nothing to do at King's College, Charing Cross is closed for repairs, and the Maternity Home has to go to fresh quarters, we undoubtedly did think it unreasonable that thirty-five Sisters, who have thrown us over, should occupy our headquarters, and we informed the Superior we were ready to relieve her at once. She declined to go before the 11th of September. This, of course, adds to our work and anxiety; we are obliged to see our ladies elsewhere, for you can have no conception what Sister Aimee, who rules there, can be at times, or what a ridiculous figure poor mankind makes having incurred her wrath. We have had one scene there which obliged me to request the Superior to keep her out of the way in future when we meet in the committee-room.[3]

Sister Caroline, Sister Aimee, and the others can scarcely have had their sympathy for "poor mankind," especially as it was exemplified by their honorary treasurer, much increased by this public version of a private correspondence, and there was worse to come.

On 8 August the *Times*, while employing its habitual judicious tone and giving the sisters full credit for zeal, devotion, "high principles and refined nurture," nevertheless stated in a long leader that the case was one of "inevitable struggle for supremacy," in which "the main issue, disengaged from personal questions and excited feeling on both sides, is whether in the practical management of the hospital the Sisters should control the Medical Staff or the Medical Staff the Sisters." The sisters, of course, had never exerted or thought of exerting such a claim, but the issue, put thus in the very familiar terms raised in 1880 during the nursing controversy at Guy's, was therefore rendered susceptible to the same resolution: "the final authority must rest with the Medical Staff."[4] Cooperation was at best only another term for subordination, and only complete subordination suited most men's—whether doctors, administrators, or journalists—ideal standard for hospital governance. The house committee were so satisfied with the *Times*'s version of the dispute that they immediately ordered 250 reprints of the piece.[5]

At the same 8 August meeting of the house committee a printed letter from Ernest Frere—secretary, and nephew of Bartle Frere—to be sent separately to each of the nurses employed by St. John's House was entered in the minutes. The committee admitted that they had been informed by the superior that the nurses now had, "with some few exceptions, tendered their resignations" in the wake of the sisters', but he asserted nevertheless that "the retirement of the Superior and Sisters will not have the least effect on St. John's House." The main body of the letter then attempted to render this assurance true by frightening the nurses into giving up their intent to resign:

> Neither the Superior nor the Sisters have any power to relieve you from your engagements to St. John's House.
> You engaged yourself for three years certain to St. John's House, and are bound to give three months' notice after

you have fulfilled that period. No one can release you from this but the Council of St. John's House.

If you break your engagement you will forfeit all wages which may be due to you, and all other advantages present and future which you may have acquired, and be liable to pay £6 as a forfeit, and to give up your regulation clothing, or we may, if we think proper, prevent you taking any other engagements until your agreed term has expired.

Promises of indemnity may have been made to you, but by whom, and what security have you?[6]

The threatening tone of this letter and its implication of dishonest dealing by the sisters are in themselves evidence for the danger of widespread resignations among the nurses, and the committee were not mistaken in their fears, whatever may be thought of their methods. The sisters probably needed to make no extravagant promises to attract women who knew and respected them. When the council's replacement for Sister Caroline made her first report she was obliged to admit that although "the work in the Hospitals, and by the private staff of nurses, has continued without interruption[, a] good many of the nurses left with the late Sisters, and more have since left to join them," while "some nurses have been dismissed,"[7] perhaps because of their visible discontent with their new supervisors.

Bartle Frere himself now returned to the task of removing the sisters from Norfolk Street, writing to Sister Caroline on 9 August: "I wish you could make it convenient to give us early possession of the house. I am sure you must agree with me that the Sisters are not mending their cause by remaining there as it affords a complete answer to any complaints of our shortcomings that the new workers are kept away from their place of business."[8] While Frere consistently maintained that Sister Caroline was an admirable woman whose good opinion he treasured, he equally consistently represented her to herself as a pawn in the hands of the unscrupulous or demented Sister Aimee. In a second letter sent the following day he warned the superior of what she certainly already knew, "that you have not the power to cancel the engagements of a single nurse. . . . If you attempt it you are misleading these women and I am certain you would not do so if acting on your own free will.—I only wish we could keep you unfettered."[9]

Sister Caroline's opinion of Frere's tactics she kept to herself, refusing to be lured into either argument or complicity. Harassed by the constant demand, both public and private, for the sisters' removal, she made arrangements to leave Norfolk Street as soon as possible, briefly notifying Frere of her plans on 13 August: "I am prepared to leave St. John's House with the remainder of the Sisters [that is, those who had not already left to stay with friends and relatives] on the 18th of this Month—August—in compliance with the urgent desire expressed by you. This will be one month and two days after their departure from the Hospital."[10] The final sentence may have reminded Frere not only of the council's original agreement to a three-month transition period but of their offer of an additional month's leave of absence as well; if not, Sister Caroline did not choose to point it out. To the sisters, however, the council's indifference to an agreement with themselves must have contrasted bitterly with the house committee's insistence on holding the nurses to the letter of their bond.

It must also have seemed to them that they packed for their hasty departure under the eyes of a largely hostile world: the *Lancet* sneered that their resignation "rather resembles the action of trades-unionists than that of philanthropic ladies,"[11] while the *Medical Times and Gazette* added to its criticism of the sisters fulsome praise of the council and the committee of management for having "been very earnest in trying to induce the Sisters to take a less exalted and more practical view of their office and functions, and hav[ing] shown great patience in the matter; but in vain."[12]

On 15 August Frere wrote again to Sister Caroline to thank her for making Norfolk Street, Strand, available, although the language he chose to use—"your having arranged to let St. John's House and Sisterhood into their headquarters"—seems unnecessarily cruel. He admitted that he had already written to the *Times* complaining of the "inconvenience occasioned by our not having the House" but stated that he had "sent a P. S. to state that the matter is arranged" and then concluded in his usual vein of insistent compliment: "If I am now saying good bye to you I wish to add, that your disapproval has been the one thing which has made me from time to time doubt whether what I have had to do was necessary and right and that it causes us great regret that you should have found it impossible to continue in charge of the work which you are so competent to manage and have so long managed in a way to command the respect and affection of all connected with it."[13] Frere's post-script appeared in the *Times* on 20 August and included the unequivocal statement that the Norfolk Street premises had now been "left, with all necessary attendance, in complete order," an assertion that would later be forgotten, and that in their departure "our sisters have done themselves honour. It increases our regret at the loss of them, but confirms what I have ventured to say of the strength secured by the co-opera-tion of mankind with good women."[14]

Given as Frere was, however, to irrational outbursts of chiv-alrous cant, he was at least consistent in excepting Sister Aimee from them. In his earlier letter to the *Times*, the one in which he had complained of the inaccessibility of the premises, he had undertaken the difficult task of proving that a sis-terhood was an ideal instrument for nursing a hospital while simultaneously explaining how St. John's House had lost its entire staff of sisters, and he had done so on his already estab-lished principle of attributing the entire blame to the mega-lomania and deceitfulness of one woman, Sister Aimee:

> Though 35 ladies are stated to have seceded, only about half that number seem to be members of the sisterhood in actual work. The full number of 35 is insignificant in com-parison with the number of good women ready trained and just as much sisters as half the alleged seceders. Many of the greatest value were extruded by our clever *maitresse femme*. She had, as she stated [Frere does not say where, and no such statement is now traceable] lost us King's Col-lege, where she was supreme, but we have recovered it. In command she would inevitably, I think, alienate Charing-cross. She is setting up a society free from the interference

of men. We do not blame her or her lieutenants for acting on her principles, but her principles, it now appears, are not those of St. John's House, and must have wrecked us sooner or later. We cannot approve her strategy. But what at first seemed likely to ruin St. John's House I am fast recognizing as fortunate. . . . We have appointed an acting Lady Superior of St. John's House, and are engaged in selecting sisters, and suffer no inconvenience but what arises from the retention for the convenience of Sister Aimee and her new institution of the head-quarters of St. John's House.[15]

That this letter actually appeared on the day of the sisters' removal can only, like the deliberate mention of Sister Aimee's name, the representation of the sisterhood as irrational man-haters, and the imputation that even their membership list was false, have hardened their resolve not to be destroyed in practice as well as in reputation by their former governors.

On 21 August, a letter from Sister Aimee appeared in several different newspapers "to let our many friends know that the old Sisterhood of St. John's continues intact with the Superior under whose wise guidance it has hitherto prospered, and will continue its work of nursing and training nurses under the title of 'The Nursing Sisters of St. John the Divine.'" She continued with what seems, compared to Frere's customary inaccuracy and innuendo, marked restraint: "There is no need to enter into the details of late events which have culminated in the departure of the Sisterhood from the house. The tone and spirit evinced in the published letters of their ex-treasurer" (as Frere had not yet carried out his stated intention to resign, Sister Aimee may have meant that he was no longer *their* treasurer) "are at once a witness to the necessity of the separation and a full justification of it. If I add that this is the third great crisis in an institution not yet more than 35 years old . . . it will suffice to show that its constitution cannot be sound."[16] Rather than recriminate over this history, she went on instead to a detailed announcement of the plans and needs of the new sisterhood, which from now on was to matter much more to the sisters than their relations with their late council. The *Church Times,* commenting on her letter, even concluded that the secession crisis might very well have been worse had it not been for the "moderation and self-restraint of Sister Aimee, . . . whose conduct hardly supports the charges . . . of masterful temper, and [that she] was in a state of chronic hostility to the doctors. If that had been the case, it seems strange that the whole thirty-five sisters should without hesitation have thrown in their lot with her; and it may be assumed that she would not so quickly have yielded place to those whom she regarded as treating her ill."[17]

The solidarity of the sisterhood indeed remained the principal unassimilable element in Frere's version of events, assuming that his suggestion that Sister Aimee had bewitched them was a figure of speech. The sisters' letters show as strong a loyalty to her as can well be imagined, and Sister Aimee's own letters are invariably, even when blunt, logical and specific. Furthermore, in spite of all of Frere's assertions to the contrary, the council were not finding the work of St. John's House easy to manage without the former sisters. Almost at once, difficulties arose in the nursing of Charing Cross Hospital, to whose officers the house committee had refused to send, probably because they were not sure of, a list of the nurses available to make up the renovated Charing Cross staff. The warden of the hospital, Richard Westhorpe, wrote on 5 September 1883, to point out that the list was needed because St. John's House was now scarcely the same institution with which Charing Cross had made its original contract:

> At the date of that Agreement St. John's House possessed a large and thoroughly experienced Staff of Sisters and Nurses, and it was on the strength of this very fact that that agreement and the proceeding [*sic*] one of 1866 were entered into.
>
> The condition of St. John's at this moment is totally at variance with its condition in either 1866 or 1877. The entire body of Sisters and (as I am informed and believe) a very large portion of the Nurses have been withdrawn from

St. John's and it is a matter of public notoriety that at this present moment the Committee in Charge of the functions of the Council of St. John's have the greatest difficulty in supplying for King's College Hospital Sisters and Nurses of competent experience to undertake the duties hitherto devolving upon the Ladies who have withdrawn from St. John's.[18]

The committee agreed to furnish the list, although their minutes do not reveal how the names were to be arrived at. At their next meeting they received without comment the resignations from the St. John's House council of Robert Few, Henry E. Butler, and Hector Monro,[19] all of whom had supported the sisters in their quarrel first with King's College and then with their own officers.

Clearly matters were not proceeding as smoothly as Frere's public statements alleged, and at the house committee's next weekly meeting resentment at the departed sisters surfaced in three pieces of business that seem primarily vindictive. The first was the honoring of Nurse Howard with the Associate Cross, already noted, the second a request for "an Inventory of the furniture belonging to St. John's House in King's College Hospital and Charing Cross Hospital to make as complete a list as possible of missing articles of furniture," and the third a letter to Sister Caroline's business agent, James Waddell, attempting to recover the accounts of the sisters' funds.[20] It can scarcely have lessened the committee's indignation that the newly formed Nursing Sisters of St. John the Divine were having some initial success, having been solicited by the bishop of Honolulu to send sisters and nurses to Hawaii, then an independent kingdom. A letter from Sister Caroline appeared in the *Times* on 20 September announcing the project and soliciting funds.[21]

In response to the rather fuzzy-minded suggestion of a governor of Charing Cross Hospital, Edward Abram, that although he knew none of the details of the dispute he thought the Christian solution should be a compromise originating with the sisters,[22] Sister Caroline wrote again, revealing that the seceding sisters had in fact offered to stay on at Charing Cross Hospital, with which they had no quarrel, if they could do so independently of their council, but that their offer had been rejected because of the council's urgent representations of the primacy of their contract. The general picture created was of a sisterhood with justice on their side, a council with only legality on theirs.

The house committee on 28 September accordingly considered recommendations from the bishops of Bedford and Lincoln on how the institution could be revitalized, the two stated ends being "1. To reorganize the Sisterhood. 2. To recover the confidence of the public,"[23] one of the few admissions the committee or council ever made that the sisterhood was in fact disorganized and public confidence shaken if not altogether lost. The bishops' probably naively well-intentioned recommendation was to place a mole in the sisterhood by appointing a chaplain who "would gain their confidence and regard by personal sympathy as well as by Spiritual offices" and, from a vantage point on the council, "watch any symptoms of discontent and discord and endeavour to prevent and check any misunderstandings." To do the bishops justice, they also recommended that the lady superior attend some council meetings and that the representation of the hospitals on the council be limited,[24] but no discussion of these proposals is recorded, and the bishop of Bedford later resigned from the house committee on grounds of overwork,[25] a possible indication that the proposition was received coolly.

For what it was worth, the *Lancet* continued to promulgate the official St. John's House view of events, that the nursing work had been only "temporarily impaired, . . . whilst the sisters have lost the care and charge of the largest institution with which they have been connected [so that] it seems doubtful whether they will be able to continue in existence as a sisterhood,"[26] but in fact relations with Charing Cross Hospital were now rapidly worsening. There had been, after all, no quarrel there comparable to that at King's College Hospital, and in fact Robert Few, Charing Cross's treasurer, had been one of the sisters' strongest defenders both on the St. John's House council and in letters to the press. It naturally seemed to Few and to a majority of his fellow officers, therefore, that Charing Cross had lost the services of a staff of sisters it valued highly only as an incidental casualty to St. John's House's over-identification with the interests of King's College Hospital,[27] and they were entirely indisposed to accept less efficient though well-intentioned nursing as a satisfactory substitute. On 9 November 1883, a large meeting of the council of Charing Cross Hospital voted to determine their contract with St. John's House "at the earliest possible period."[28]

Bartle Frere, meanwhile, continued as honorary treasurer of St. John's House, refusing to admit that he had made any mistakes, continuing to present Sister Aimee as the institution's Iago, and asserting—less than two weeks before the contract with Charing Cross Hospital was to be formally determined—that the retention of the two major hospitals vindicated all his actions. Monro's letter of resignation, read at the 29 October meeting of the council, argued that Frere's and Bell's hostility to the sisters had been a major cause of their secession, and Frere, as he had done before, offered to resign, but the majority of the council, as he probably expected, asked him to stay at his post and, as usual, inserted his latest denunciatory letter in their minutes. As the gap widened between the sort of success Frere had envisioned and the increasingly tarnished one he seemed to have won his language grew more extravagant and his resentment of Sister Aimee more intense:

> She has carried off her Sisters to "Patmos" [the name of the house where the new nursing order had its headquarters] freed from the embarrassment of a Council of Men. She has used every expedient (some not in my opinion creditable or consistent with her high pretensions) to carry off the Nursing Staff and to divert the work to her new Institution. She left us avowedly because she did not like us and thought she could do better for herself elsewhere. She loses no opportunity of informing the public of her complete success. She assures us she is "doing famously"—has, she says, all the best nurses, plenty of money, houses rent-free, and is courted by a Foreign Potentate. No Men are in "Patmos" to

dispute her will but Mr. Few who publishes his implicit belief in everything she tells him, and her Brother-in-law who has come valiantly forward now under one pseudonym and now under another to advocate her cause. What has she or what have her followers to complain of? How can she be otherwise than grateful to the men she so scorns and whose yoke she has cast off for accepting her resignation?[29]

As usual when Frere purports to be quoting Sister Aimee, the language is lurid and no source documents are to be found; since it is also inconsistent with all of Sister Aimee's writing that we have it seems probable that Frere believed himself to be quoting her thoughts. In any case, a potentially more effective forum than a defensive letter to his brother councillors was now available to him in the official form of the St. John's House annual report, a summary of which appeared in the Times, where it would receive maximum publicity, on 21 November. In addition to giving yet again the council's version of the crisis over Dr. Hayes and Sister Aimee's dismissal, the report now publicly charged the seceding sisters with seducing nurses and with having taken away with them the accounts—not, as yet, the money—of the sisters' fund.[30]

What seems most to have exacerbated relations between the sisters and their former council at this point, however, was an ill-considered public statement on behalf of the latter charging the former with a variety of moral and possibly legal failings. While everyone referred to this "statement" repeatedly, however, no one seems to have preserved a copy—evidence, perhaps, that the house committee ultimately found its assertions embarrassingly difficult to support after it had made them. It was nevertheless this document that Sister Caroline referred to when she addressed a printed letter to the bishop of Bedford describing in detail a correspondence she had had with one nurse, only part of which had been quoted by Bell, the principal author of the "statement," in an effort to prove that the sisters were subverting the nurses' loyalty and also going into considerable detail about the furnishings of the house whose ownership was now, rather belatedly, being disputed. Her letter concludes bitterly: "Who of the Council has asked me since I left, for one article of furnishings? For any picture, book, or ornament, which they conceive to belong to the House? Which of them asked me for anything removed (as is now averred) from King's College wrongfully, while I was still at St. John's House, for a whole month after the Sisters were desired to and did leave the Hospital? *Not one.*"³¹ In a supplementary letter direct to the *Times* she added in response to a charge made in the annual report, "No account-books whatsoever have been removed from St. John's House by myself of by any of the Sisterhood. Such account books as the treasurer may have possessed, which I presume were shown to the auditors when they annually certified the account, must be in his keeping still."³²

The sisters now addressed their former honorary secretary, George William Bell, through a firm of solicitors, seeking to recover a misappropriated letter addressed to Sister Aimee which had been mistakenly supposed to show her dealing improperly with nursing fees (in fact, as Few explained later, it was a business letter relating to a sum of money paid on account to a decorating firm and had nothing whatsoever to do with nursing)³³ and asking rather menacingly if the council intended their implication that the sisters had committed embezzlement—if they had, then they were asked to name their solicitors.³⁴ The house committee in their reply refused to give up Sister Aimee's letter but avowed that the sisters' reading of the "Statement" was inaccurate. As an internal letter of their own reveals, however, they had in fact lost Sister Aimee's letter and decided it was a better policy to refuse to surrender it than to admit the truth.³⁵

It seems impossible at this point to acquit the officers and house committee of St. John's House of active malice toward their former sisterhood, at least during the winter of 1883–84, when their own recovery from the secession was proceeding far less smoothly than they publicly claimed and the energetic launching of the Nursing Sisters of St. John the Divine was getting a good deal of favorable public attention—and money. Few's pamphlet details the house committee's hopeful search for faults on the part of the sisters:

What has been the *modus operandi to make out a case against these ladies . . . ? a hunt after possible information* is determined upon, and to this end the nurses are cross-examined as to *whether they have any tales to tell against the ladies. . . .* The next person from whom evidence was sought was the carpenter who was employed by the Sisters, and not only did one of the Council—so he designated himself—say "we want to know what the sisters have taken from St. John's, and to this end we want you to go to our solicitors . . . and answer such questions as they may put to you," but, seeing that he did not go to the solicitors they came to him, and spent, he says, half an hour interrogating him as to what he could say the Sisters took away. . . . "Never," said the man to me, "*did I see such a persecution of ladies as this.*"[36]

Few was certainly almost as biased in the sisters' favor as Frere and Bell were against them, but his assertion that the committee were more than anxious to receive information discrediting them seems to be borne out by their action in raising the wages of the Norfolk Street housekeeper from £32 to £40 per annum at the same meeting at which she presented them with a statement detailing allegedly missing property.[37] If she was not, like Nurse Howard, being rewarded for services rendered, then the statement and the pay raise were a remarkable and unfortunate coincidence.

It was also during this period (on 6 December 1883) that the *Times*'s leader referred to by Few as obviously emanating from King's College Hospital appeared. It not only, as Few had asserted, referred to anecdotal material but described St. John's House as having been founded with the "primary object"[38] of improving the nursing at King's College Hospital, a misstatement against which the council raised no objection. As the sisters had warned, in fact, St. John's House was now, practically speaking, at the mercy of King's College Hospital, which naturally pressed its advantage. In a confidential report dated 10 December from a subcommittee appointed by the committee of management on 18 July, immediately after the exclusion of the sisterhood from the hospital, recommendations were made which tended not only to strip St. John's House workers of any independence they might have retained but also to make the council completely obedient to the committee. Professing a wish to continue its work with St. John's House, the subcommittee nevertheless asked for "an early determination of the Agreement at present in force, and the substitution for it of a Contract embodying the amendments recommended in this report."[39]

Neither the council nor the house committee recorded any response to this document—they were perhaps too preoccupied by the dilemma posed them by hostile public opinion. In spite of the support of the medical press and the *Times*, the *Church Times* and *Guardian* still supported the sisters, and the sisters themselves were making a good job of presenting their case convincingly. On 18 December, Sister Caroline sent to the *Times* a copy of her 23 November letter to the bishop of Bedford. Explaining that she had first addressed it not only to the bishop but "to the patron, to the president, and to every member of the Council of St. John's House" but had received not only no replies but no acknowledgments of its receipt, she went on to follow the advice of her friends and publish the letter in defence of herself and the rest of the sisterhood.[40] The whole sequence of her actions seems fair-minded and judicious, and the house committee recognized that their own failure to respond had hurt their reputation. In a long letter to the council, printed but not published, the house committee nevertheless opposed making any public reply, alleging instead "that it is much to be desired that there should be an end of what is now an unprofitable controversy, and that it is in vain to attempt to correct public opinion by further discussions."[41]

To the council, however, "some members of which are absent from London" and some of whom, moreover, may have begun to doubt the wisdom of the committee to which they had handed over their affairs, the committee asserted still that their charges against the sisters were well founded and that "Miss Lloyd's [that is, Sister Caroline's] complaints can be satisfactorily refuted or explained," though the committee's letter in fact failed to do either, depending instead on reiteration rather than proof to make its points.[42] The mysterious matter of the sisters' fund was discussed at length but clarified. The status of the fund as a part of the house rather than the property of the sisters existing at any given moment was rehearsed yet again, and the assertion made that contributions to it had been made not only by "the retiring Sisters, but many members of the Council, and friends of the House and Sisterhood, including Sisters who remain loyal to St. John's House," a group whose very existence is doubtful. In fact, although they were unable to improve their case for the allegations they had made already, the committee now carried them further: "So far as can be judged from the information accessible to the Treasurer, there are very considerable sums of money to be accounted for, both as regards the Sisters and the Lady Pupils, and the necessary Accounts are withheld."[43]

As both Few in his pamphlet and the sisters' solicitor in a letter to the house committee pointed out, the only precedent for the present case was that set by Sister Mary Jones, who in 1868 had asked for and received the whole of the sisters' fund as it then stood. The fund had been restarted under the acting superior, Mrs. Hodson, and Sister Aimee—who as Sister Caroline's agent had kept track of it ever since in a "temporary day-book"— had occasionally given funds to the accountant or secretary and received receipts from them.[44] No accounts beyond these had been kept by the sisters, who seem to have believed that independent records were kept (as indeed it seems they should have been) by the treasurer, and the fund thus typifies that faulty constitution which Sister Aimee herself had pointed out as central to St. John's House's recurring problems. No one really knew what amount of money was at stake or what accounts had been kept of it: the institution's bylaws had left the fund entirely a matter of custom. The sisters' solicitor was sure enough of his case to threaten to take it to court, asking even for money contributed to the fund since their departure,[45] and on 25 February 1884 the house committee instructed the secretary to write, informing him that they intended no further action.[46]

The officials and house committee of St. John's House had scarcely succeeded in their objective: destroying the sisterhood had not saved it. St. John's House never recovered its former standing as an independent nursing organization, allying itself first to the All Saints Sisterhood, then to the community of St. Peter, and finally to St. Thomas's Hospital to eke out its departed sisterhood. It ceased to exist in 1919,[47] while the Nursing Sisters of St. John the Divine, which became a fully religious order in 1930, still functions independently today.[48] The final report in the lady superior's book comes from midsummer 1885 and states, "It has been found successful as well as desirable to discontinue the nursing at King's College Hospital. The arrangements for severing the connexion are being conducted amicably, and on July 31st St. John's House ceases to nurse King's College Hospital."[49] Amicability, as Sister Aimee and her co-workers had foreseen, had proved an insufficient principle, and its proponents on the council can scarcely have been pleased to find their former champions at the *Lancet* opining that their experience proved that "nursing by sisterhoods has been tried and found unsatisfactory, notably in Guy's" (which had never employed a sisterhood at all) "and King's College,"[50] where they had taken such extreme measures to make the sisters fully amenable to the medical staff and committee of management.

As the *Guardian* had observed in a leader supporting the sisters after their secession, Bartle Frere and his party had never really "got hold of the idea of a 'Sisterhood.' . . . For all efficient purposes, for all that the Christian public of England cares, and for all that the suffering poor in our Hospitals want, the Sisters are St. John's House."[51] Certainly by maintaining the opposite view the officers of St. John's House ended by losing not only the sisterhood but the nursing of two major hospitals and a good deal of their own public credibility and support. The undismayed sisterhood, perhaps not entirely regretting the charged political atmosphere and contests for status of a major teaching hospital, devoted itself to the work it had always had at heart, nursing. At the time of the publication of Few's pamphlet in 1884, they continued to provide nurses for private families, operated a "Lying-In House for Poor Married Women" in Chelsea and district homes in Poplar and Lewisham, and were projecting not only their exotic venture to "New Zealand and the Sandwich Islands" but a children's hospital in Lewisham.[52] As Sister Laura had written in 1868, "*You* evidently as a council thought much of the prestige of your name. *We* did not weigh it for a moment. It was absolutely nothing to us."[53] Surprisingly enough, the sisters' intransigence proved in the end more flexible, and finally more successful, than their officers' compromises and manipulations of power: the sisters, unlike the council, knew not only what they wanted but what they were willing to pay for it, and they survived to see their course vindicated by events.

PART FOUR
Conclusions

At both Guy's and King's College hospitals, the "new" nurses, most of them formally trained upper- and middle-class women, had had to fight hard for their objectives, and their success had not been complete. Neither, however, had they failed nearly so entirely as their opponents liked to claim. As Cameron rather grudgingly admitted in his history of Guy's Hospital, "the reforms of the self-assured and ruthless Miss Burt had done their work. The nurses had become nurses."[1] When the controversial former matron died in 1892 a memorial tablet was placed in the Guy's Hospital chapel "as a token of Esteem and Affection / by a few Friends and Fellow-workers"; its brief and somewhat cryptic epitaph reads, "She hath done what she could"—less, certainly, than she must have hoped, but more than the hostile medical staff and their supporters in the press had ever been willing to admit.

The sisters of St. John's House, once they had given up that institution and reorganized themselves as the Nursing Sisters of St. John the Divine, were ultimately able to claim a similar victory: they had maintained their principles in spite of great pressure to abandon them and had persuaded a significant part of the public of the justice of their cause. The example of their expulsion from King's College Hospital and of its consequences would have been fresh in everyone's mind when in 1886 the All Saints Sisterhood, which served

University College Hospital, was attacked for sectarian bias when it refused to accept a nonconformist applicant for membership (it did hire nonconformist nurses). In spite of letters to the press and the raking up of all the old arguments against sisterhoods as deficient in loyalty to the hospitals they served, both the staff and governors in this case stood firmly behind the sisterhood, and the would-be scandal at last died away in some discomfiture for those who had made the initial complaint. The All Saints Sisterhood remained at University College Hospital until 1899, perhaps the beneficiary of the loss of public support for King's College Hospital after the St. John's House sisters had been obliged to leave their posts.[2]

As Dr. Lionel S. Beale had put it in his introductory lecture to the incoming medical students at King's College Hospital back in October 1873:

No calling has undergone more wonderful changes—and for the better—in these last days than that of nurse, nursing sister, and superintendent of nurses. Nursing has become a profession, and in some hospitals—I wish I could say in all—a special department. The old "matrum" and her poor, overworked, ignorant, scrubbing attendants, have either disappeared or have much changed in character. . . . The system did seem bad, and according to my experience it certainly was desperately bad, but no doubt it had its good points. . . . Every old nurse was eminently deferential, and in a way thoroughly under the control of the constituted authorities. Though the discipline seemed lax in some particulars, and the work was often most carelessly performed, there was never any doubt as to who was master and who served. . . . Nurses are now of an altogether different order. They are taken from a different class. They are, I may say, well educated. They are trained, and know their work. Many are proud of nursing the sick, but few will scrub the floor. Nurses are paid higher wages. They are devoted and trustworthy, but are of course more independent. Hospital nursing nowadays may be thoroughly well done, but of course it is more costly than the apology wrongly called nursing in former days. Still, at this time there exist two very different ideas of what a nurse ought to be. According to one, she is a sort of medical maid-of-all-work, to be generally useful; according to the other, she is a member of a profession, and has rights as well as duties. For the last twenty years many medical practitioners have been doing their utmost to raise the character of the nurse and increase her efficiency.[3]

As Beale implied, however, many of his colleagues were not so supportive. Beale himself, after taking a very active part in defense of the sisterhood in 1874, seems to have kept out of the controversy of 1883, writing no surviving letters and apparently leaving the leadership of meetings to others—in effect, to the house's officers, whose view of a nursing sister's calling was not the one advocated in his lecture. The reasons for Beale's personal inaction are unknown, but the basic reason why so many of his colleagues opposed the increased training and improved status of nurses is clear from the lecture itself: they perceived in the phenomenon of the "new" nurse a threat to their own eminence.

Throughout this period, certainly, there was a marked rise in both the reputation and the actual competence of hospital nurses. At the same time, however, medical men, on a considerably shakier basis so far as any real advance in their ability to diagnose and treat patients was concerned, were also preoccupied with prestige and status, and they seem to have regarded nurses as doubly threatening. Not only did nurses lay claim to their own sphere of medical expertise but they were also women, inherently threatening to a wholly male medical profession thoroughly persuaded of patriarchal values. That a hospital should be regarded as equivalent to a private (male) citizen's domicile or, in the other comparison frequently evoked in nineteenth-century nursing conflicts, an empire was a metaphor having for the male medical profession the force of unquestioned fact. As an unidentified correspondent wrote in the *British Medical Journal* in 1883, "the dictates of common sense . . . require that every man shall be master in his own house."[4] Doctors saw themselves as by rights patriarchal rulers, undervalued and mistreated if they were asked to cooperate with nurses, and also as appropriate authorities for the generality of their contemporaries: their aspirations hardly ceased at the mere domination of hospitals.

In his inaugural address as principal of King's College and dean of its medical faculty in 1884, the Reverend Dr. Henry Wace, after congratulating Lister and Bowman on their recent honors, went on to praise the profession at large for its recent gains in status:

> It was familiar to all how largely the medical profession had gained during recent generations in the honour and gratitude with which it was regarded. So long as medicine or surgery appeared mainly as an empiric art, remedying a passing accident to the human body or simply helping it through some of its physical struggles, it might, indeed, establish innumerable claims to personal gratitude, but its wide and far-reaching possibilities of influencing all human development were necessarily obscure. . . . The medical profession had of late been revealing . . . more and more of the subtle secrets of [humanity's] constitution, and thus guiding them along many an obscure path. It was one of the most striking instances of the good which in this world was so continually educed from evil, that the diseases and accidents of individual sufferers should have been the occasion for experiments and researches which had brought benefits to the whole of their race. The sick in their hospitals were to a large extent the vicarious sufferers for the rest of mankind and the sacrifices of their painful experience won blessings, through the agency of the medical profession, for mankind at large. The students . . . had now gained a point at which the world felt that they must be consulted, not merely in death and disease, but in life and action, and people were looking to them for principles and rules which would determine, not only their daily conduct, but the administration of Government and the general organization of the community.[5]

The whole world, of course, was scarcely ready to go so far as this in entrusting itself to medical men, but to many of the profession this reluctance only demonstrated the world's folly and the unfair liabilities under which their profession suffered—for instance, as the *Times* stated on the occasion of the opening lectures at the medical schools in October 1883, its comparative lack of opportunities to address the public and persuade them of its views.[6]

When such opportunities did arise, however, the profession was not shy in the use it made of them. At the 1886 meeting of the British Medical Association in Brighton the incoming president, Dr. Withers Moore, addressed his assembled brethren on two issues of special grievance: inadequate fees and the threat posed to the future of the human race by the higher education of women. Under the first heading he denounced "gratuitous medical relief" as " 'eating out whatever of manly independence may have been left in the poorer classes, and at the same time rendering the struggles of the general practitioner more severe,' " and proposed that if the most prestigious London physicians were to charge greatly increased fees they would have fewer patients and more leisure without a decline in income, and that those patients who could no longer afford their advice would then turn to "practitioners not as yet of the first eminence," who could improve their skills on this newly available population. The argument is reminiscent of Dr. Wace's enthusiasm for the role of hospital patients as "vicarious sufferers" for all of humanity—or in practice, for the middle and upper classes of British society. Moore also, of course, believed that patients would ultimately benefit, although only as a rather remote final consequence: "as the circle went on widening, there would ensue such a diffusion of work (and wages) as would have the effect of largely augmenting the total amount of practical power and promptitude in the profession, and thereby also of benefit at once available for the sick and suffering worlds of their patients."[7]

Despite Dr. Moore's claims for his scheme, it is obvious that increased income rather than the care of patients was its principal motive, and it is scarcely surprising if, when such views were common and openly expressed, the "outer world" was, as the *Medical Times and Gazette* had observed during the Guy's Hospital controversy, "only too apt to believe the worst of the most beneficent profession that has ever existed."[8] The profession almost certainly exaggerated the public's distrust as well as its own altruism, but there was distrust, and much of it was justified. Wace's claims for the scientific authority of medical knowledge were at the very least premature. The all-round failure of diagnosis and treatment in the Ingle case illustrates the point, and the profession's ignorance of and authoritarianism about the biological character of women are relevant both to its hostility toward nurses as trained medical personnel and to its treatment of women as patients. Patricia Branca has summed up the state of its knowledge in the special field of obstetrics and gynecology at the time as "minimal":

> The functions of the ovaries and fallopian tubes were not even vaguely known. Though menstrual disorders were considered important there was incomplete understanding of the menstrual cycle. As late as the 1880s, it was described in an article in the *British Medical Journal* as "an accidental and incidental phenomena." Even among the specialists on women's health there was serious lack of knowledge. The consequences of this were that many theories and practices were used which were totally ineffective. Nineteenth-century gynecology was greatly limited by its approach, which involved an eternal search for the universal answer to each and every female disorder. With the introduction of the speculum the focus was on the uterus as being the cause of all female ills. In another phase of development gynecologists contended that all female problems were a matter of disorders of the menstrual cycle. In addition it should be realized that uterine disorders were not common health problems for most women. The advances made by the pioneers helped the gynecologists and obstetricians gain respectability and prestige in the field of medicine but in reality offered little for the average women of any social class.[9]

Doctors eked out their ignorance of women's real biological natures with what they unquestioningly believed to be true about women both physically and spiritually. In the second part of his presidential address, Dr. Moore therefore undertook what he saw as the proper medical role of taking his knowledge and "apply[ing] it to the actual use and benefit of mankind in the person of [his and his colleagues'] patients," considering for this purpose "what is called the higher education of women, . . . which aims at raising women (as it imagines) to the masculine level, by fitting them for the exercise of brain-power in competition with men." Although he began with a long sequence of rhetorical questions ("Is it for the good of the human race . . . that we should have female doctors and divines, lawyers, mathematicians, and astronomers, professors, publicists, and Ministers of State?"), there can have been no suspense in his audience about the correct answers. Following directly on Moore's expressed anxiety about fees, the vision of competing female doctors was certain to intensify an already existing hostility, and the speaker's invocation of the "old chivalrous ideal" of the woman who waits at home for her lord to return, ready to "lend her ear to his tale of doing or of suffering and reward him with her gentle sympathy and loving appreciation," only served as a preliminary to his warning that women who left that sphere for "the conflict where cuffs are going . . . must be content to be cuffed and cuff back again" without the protection of chivalry.

The central argument of Moore's address, however, was not this understandable though unseemly one about competition and conflict but the popular pseudoscientific dogma that women's biological destiny as mothers would be interfered with by their education. Citing "an Oxford tutor," Galton's *Hereditary Genius*, Herbert Spencer, and a rather miscellaneous group of doctors and school inspectors whose conclusions went well beyond their data, Moore concluded to his own, and presumably his audience's, satisfaction: "Excessive work, especially in youth, is ruinous to health, both to mind and body; excessive brain work more surely so than any other. From the eagerness of women's nature, competitive brain work among gifted girls can hardly but be excessive, especially if the competition be against the superior brain weight and brain strength of man. The resulting ruin can be averted—if it be averted at all—only by drawing so largely upon the woman's whole capital stock of vital force and energy as to leave a remainder quite inadequate for maternity."[10]

It is important to stress that this theory was by no means an aberration of Dr. Moore's, unshared by the majority of his peers (it was, for instance, paraphrased approvingly in the *Journal of American Medicine*).[11] In an 1881 article the editors of the *Lancet*, treating the subject for by no means the first time, wrote,

> In the ordinance of nature the female is endowed with a force tending to the reproduction from her arrested or suppressed organism of the perfect organism of the male. It is essential to the accomplishment of this physiological task that the female should be trained for the development of *capacity*—that is receptivity—as a cerebral property, rather than impressed with the particular bias of education in a special class of subjects, or on formulated lines. . . . Experience seems to show that special brain-*work*, properly so called, exhausts the energy of brain-development . . . which, if conserved, would express itself in the mental perfection of her male offspring.[12]

The consequences of such beliefs as these were many, but one of the most important for nurses was the indignation felt by the male medical profession when women failed to conform to them. The conduct of such women, as described by, again, the *Lancet* in an attack on women medical students in 1876, was clearly motivated by sheer perversity: "If those women who are seeking, at an extravagant cost of time and money, to enter the medical profession, were *content* to work in the only department of medical practice which is properly open to them— namely, as midwives and nurses,—no objection could fairly be raised, provided that they always practiced under the supervision of qualified medical practitioners. . . . But . . . the female medical students in London . . . [have as their] *ambition* . . . to be placed upon the Medical Register, and then to *please themselves* what branches of medical practice they shall engage in."[13] Ambition and its satisfactions were not appropriate in women; contentment was. When Miss Burt at Guy's Hospital and Sister Aimee at King's College initiated changes or criticized the performance of medical men they were not only disruptive but unfeminine, a condition so alarming that even Cameron, in whose opinion Miss Burt's reforms were reasonable and effective, nevertheless felt constrained to call her "ruthless" and "self-assured." It seems unlikely that self-assurance would have been considered discreditable in a doctor, but in a woman it was threatening, as it clearly was also in Sister Aimee, before whom "poor mankind" trembled.

That Bartle Frere seriously envisioned as an important part of every nurse's training at King's College Hospital the development of a capacity for adapting to the varied and imperfect characters of medical men with no reciprocal education for doctors similarly supports the conclusion that a conventional understanding of gender rather than any abstract principle of equity or even of efficiency in the workplace was at the center of the period's disputes between nurses and doctors. As Dr. Andrew Clark, the senior physician of the London Hospital, expressed this premise in an address to an audience of ladies and nurses at the beginning of a popular course on nursing in 1881, "self-sacrifice and humility" were the qualities to strive for,[14] and although doctors and their supporters less often wrote of the consequences of nurses' failure to achieve them than in this exhortatory vein their actions when they found themselves challenged or criticized speak amply of their outrage and anger. Indeed, this medical distrust of women lasted well beyond the nursing controversies of the late nineteenth century, surfacing notably in the antisuffrage campaign of the early twentieth, when the prominent physician Almroth Wright wrote probably the most vituperative attack on the suffragists printed at the time (provoking the resentment of even antisuffrage women)[15] and medical students played a prominent role in antisuffragette rioting.[16]

Preoccupied with problems of income and reputation, medical men resented both alterations in their routines and criticism which might damage their image as a profession. The staffs of the great London teaching hospitals stood at that pro-

fession's head, persuaded both of their own importance and of
the public's failure to appreciate and reward them adequately.
Serving without pay and therefore convinced of their own mag-
nanimity, they were able for the most part to overlook the fact
that their positions gave them a reputation and status that
brought the wealthiest patients to their private consulting
rooms, even though, as Cameron noted, those patients came in
part because of the great "indirect value" of hospital staff appointments, which was so significant that one Victorian treasurer of Guy's estimated the "market price of a vacancy" there
at about five thousand pounds.[17]

Staff appointments were in fact plums and were eagerly com-
peted for (with an advantage frequently accruing to relatives
and friends) by medical students, who were also indoctrinated
in an intense and uncritical allegiance to their mentors, the
exemplars of professional success. A physician who was a student at Guy's during the early 1880s wrote of his education,
"Without any teaching from our chiefs except their example,
loyalty was the essence of what we learned at Guy's then. I
never heard a member of the staff speak disparagingly of his
colleagues. . . . We were as proud of being Guy's men as any
guardsman of his regiment."[18] This state of mind, hostile to
criticism and reveling in the consciousness of superiority, could
only generate and nurture the attitudes and actions taken by
the medical staff and student body of Guy's during the nursing
dispute.

Esprit de corps had as its underside a resistance to change
and fear of diversity and innovation that not only envenomed
specific controversies but also could and sometimes certainly
did lead both to injustice and to bad medical practice, as in the
profession's resistance to increasing and inevitable specialization. While its opposition was based theoretically on the principle that disease was a "manifestation of a widespread under-
lying state" (a general idea with such specific and erroneous
consequences as the blaming of most women's illnesses on uter-
ine and menstrual disorders), the most important reason why
the "hospital and medical school elites" opposed specialization
was that it "took organizational forms," notably the founding

of numerous specialized hospitals, "which threatened their institutions and authority."[19] The consultants of the London teaching hospitals, divided only into the two traditional professional groups of physicians and surgeons, were all by definition generalists. It was thus that Dr. Pavy, in reality a specialist in diabetes but formally a professor of general hospital practice, was called upon to diagnose Louisa Morgan and did so wrongly, in terms of the supposedly universal feminine weakness of hysteria, and thus too that he so greatly resented the challenging of his diagnosis by Sir William Gull. Professional solidarity demanded otherwise.

Notwithstanding its failures, however, the medical profession largely succeeded in its campaign to elevate its public standing. Nurses also succeeded, but since their goals had been from the first less prodigious their success has had considerably less public impact. Despite the fears of the medical men, they had never sought control of a hospital or the authority to give orders to doctors. Doctors, however, had sought and gained such power, as the demand for places on the hospital governing body raised and in part acceded to at Guy's Hospital shows. Along with a public reputation for "science" which potentially screened every practitioner however mediocre, this increased authority was sufficient by the twentieth century to make doctors almost the public mentors Wace had envisioned—and concordantly to reduce the status of nurses, in spite of all their real gains in skill and commitment, to that of the medical maids of all work Beale had believed in 1874 to be rapidly disappearing.

Centrally at stake in the hospital controversies of the 1870s and 1880s was professional status, obviously still an issue in hospitals today. Doctors undoubtedly possessed it, nor were they likely to lose it, but a professional identity is most valuable to its owners if its rewards, including its label, are kept scarce. Thus, although Dr. Beale had considered nursing a "profession, [having] rights as well as duties," others, notably the editors of the *Lancet*, disagreed, and the status of professional is still not routinely granted to nurses today. Instead, an attempt has been made to categorize nursing as a "semiprofession," partly because its training is shorter than doctors', but also, rather circularly, because its "professional authority" is less. Furthermore, as Amitai Etzioni, the originator of this designation, observes, "Part of the problem is due to the fact that the typical professional is a male where the typical semi-professional is a female. Despite the effects of emancipation, women on the average are more amenable to administrative control than men."[1]

In spite of their putative docility, however, twentieth-century women, like their Victorian predecessors, have evidently been less amenable to control than their superiors have thought appropriate, at least in the groups—nurses, teachers, and social workers—studied by Etzioni and his sociological colleagues; otherwise, it is difficult to grasp the rationale for their study, which promises that after some initial resentment members of these groups will achieve "greater self-analysis and understanding. . . . Once it is recognized that there is a middle ground [that is, status as semiprofessionals], inauthentic aspirations and positions are more likely to be renounced and the dysfunctional consequences of attempts to pass will tend to disappear."[2] The expectation is apparently the same as that held by misogynist medical men and their lay supporters in the nineteenth century—once women had had their limitations explained to them they would accept the truth and play the role nature had designed. If they did not, due to an "aspiring" tendency, as *Lancet* put it, or the "eagerness" Moore noted in "gifted girls," then their behavior was reprehensible and retribution—"cuffs"—could follow.

Etzioni and his colleagues, owing to the relative detachment of their own position as academic sociologists, are less interested than the embattled Victorian doctors were in the controversies that ensued when women would not stay in their place, but they are not less aware of the phenomenon. In an essay called "Women and Bureaucracy in the Semi-Professions," Ida Harper Simpson and Richard Simpson outline the female personality type that Victorian doctors hoped unavailingly to find at their sides in hospitals as if it were a normative reality:

> Women's values and goals make many of them tractable subordinates. Their low work commitment makes some women welcome an easy job that makes few demands, and it is easier to follow instructions than to exercise judgment. They tend to want friendly relations with co-workers and are often afraid to risk these for the sake of autonomy and power. Relatively unambitious, on the average, they are not willing to fight for advancement. They tend to be more interested in giving personal service to clients than in technical mastery of skills or in professional prerogatives to define how their skills will be put to use. Their unsure position in any situation where they might have to exercise power over men contributes to their willingness to

submit to bureaucratic control. Semi-professional women do not strive to establish independence or collegial authority patterns.[3]

At every point, of course, this description is the exact opposite of the truth about Miss Burt, Sister Aimee, and the St. John's House sisterhood. Victorian nurses, however, although they clearly possessed in a high degree the "kinds of occupational ideologies and colleague reference group orientations that are built upon specialized knowledge and strong work commitment" which the Harpers posit as requisite for professional status, were not rewarded for them. Functioning as "colleague reference groups [which] set standards of work, enforce[d] norms, and reward[ed] good performance through the colleague prestige system,"[4] they were instead charged with espionage, disloyalty, and "knowing too much."

Because nurses were and overwhelmingly still are women, their meeting professional criteria has more often than not been perceived not as an acheivement but as unfeminine behavior. Then and now, their actual medical knowledge has been derogated, even though twentieth-century nurses study as long as Victorian doctors did to receive their credentials and their curricula are not watered-down versions of those served to medical students. As Jo Ann Ashley put it, "Continuous responsibility for the care of those confined to hospital beds is still a unique function of the nursing profession,"[5] and one of its consequences is considerable differentiation in education and experience between doctors and nurses—each group knows things the other does not, a more important fact than who knows "more" and who "less" for the performance of their jobs and for the patients who receive the performance.

Nevertheless, the knowledge and training of nurses are still frequently reduced in the public mind to a sort of intuitive hand-holding—TLC (tender loving care), as Fred E. Katz in his essay on the status of nurses consistently and whimsically calls it. Katz sees nurses as outsiders in hospitals, tolerated rather than integral to their work: "in an age of high regard for science, hospitals harness both scientific and non-scientific resources for the care and treatment of patients. They do this chiefly by *admitting* the non-scientific, care-minded nurse into the hospital. In return for the right to practice non-scientific, nurturent [sic] care that has no clear place in the medical textbooks, the nurse *accepts* a low place in the hospital's status hierarchy."[6] The distinction here between scientific and non-scientific is of course considerably sharper than it is in practice—the examinations nurses pass are primarily scientific—and the social contract formulation obscures the real conditions under which nurses are generally obliged to accept their low status.[7] Katz, however, insists upon his definition of nurses' tasks as nonscientific, inadvertently revealing as he does so the fallibility of the otherwise unquestioned adequacy of "science" as the hospital's defining characteristic: the nurse, among other things, is to help to "prevent knowledge concerning errors, ambiguities, and uncertainties from reaching the patients and their families. She virtually takes over where scientific methods are inadequate or non-existent, as in the case of incurable or senile patients."[8]

Katz recognizes that the hospital as he describes it is a caste system, based on irrational, often simply false, distinctions: "Although the nurse will occasionally learn a great deal about a patient from her direct dealings with him, her knowledge and her interpretations are regarded as less valid and less 'educated' than those of the physician. The point here is not 'who knows most?' but 'who is the rightful knower?'"[9] Furthermore, "the nurse is expected to react with moral passivity to her knowledge of happenings in the hospital. Doctors' mistakes are not to be discussed—not with doctors, not with hospital administrators, and least of all with patients and outsiders in the community. While her own mistakes can be openly and drastically censured within the hospital, exposure of those by physicians is strongly tabooed, and the nurse herself helps to enforce the taboo. . . . She is expected, at all times, to protect the good name of the physician and the hospital, even if this means blocking or distorting information for public consumption."[10] Not only nurses, that is, suffer from the low status of nurses— patients do as well, but a nurse who, lacking the requisite "moral passivity," takes on the role of patient advocate, as Margaret Lonsdale did with Dr. Moxon or Sister Aimee with Dr. Hayes, soon finds herself outside the hospital, sacrificed to the "taboo" protecting the physician's and hospital's "good name."

Katz does acknowledge that "physicians generally hold the nurse in low esteem, [being] willing to see nurses receive income infinitely smaller than their own, and frequently treat-[ing] the nurse as a non-person who can be ignored and reprimanded with impunity."[11] Nevertheless, he sees the value of "science" as so great that it makes the status of physicians impregnable. Thus, nursing needs two things in order to become a profession; a better defined and recognized corpus of knowledge (a science of its own), and the replacement of caste systems in hospitals with colleagueship. Katz fails to suggest how the second objective could possibly be achieved without the cooperation of physicians—which he does not posit, and which both the history of the two groups and his own description of doctors' present privileged relations with nurses render extremely unlikely.

Given the accuracy of Katz's description, it is not at all surprising that William J. Goode, in his essay "The Theoretical Limits of Professionalization," concludes that "within the medical situs, none [of the groups seeking professional status] will achieve it." The significant possible exception is veterinary medicine, which is practiced in a separate setting not already dominated by physicians. Since among the occupations that will, according to Goode, "achieve professionalism over the next generation" are "social work, marital counseling, and perhaps city planning"[12] it seems obvious that a scientific body of knowledge is not the essential criterion—what is needed is vigorous self-promotion on the part of the group and the absence of any previously entrenched profession barring the way.

The traditional and most firmly established professions remain law, medicine, university teaching, and the ministry, all of which share, as Goode says, the traits of "cohesion, commitment to norms of service, percentage of members remaining in the profession throughout their lifetime, homogeneity of membership, [and] control over professional violations."[13] Cohesion and commitment to norms of service Victorian nurses certainly had; the St. John's House sisters were as well committed to life membership in the institution, drawn from a homogeneous class background, and highly concerned with avoiding what they perceived as professional violations. It was precisely their strong resemblance to a profession which led to their officers' determination to discipline them. As Goode inadvertently explains with an apposite illustration, "how much knowledge the profession possesses is defined in part by the society itself. The witch doctor may have very little valid knowledge, but by the canons of truth of his society he may have a great deal. But we need not move so culturally distant as the witch doctor; the physician until the later nineteenth century is an equally good example."[14] It may now seem to have been their status rather than their knowledge that the medical staffs of Guy's and King's College hospitals were most concerned to protect from the apparent encroachments of nurses, but it was a part of their identity as a profession to confound rather than to distinguish the two.

Also confounded in their arguments were the fact that they themselves were (and their profession largely still is) male, as all of the traditional professions were male, while nurses were female, and their belief that they possessed certain scientific knowledge about the biological and moral nature of women. It was thus that the canons of professionalism were and continue to be stacked against women. Katz criticizes the lack of commitment of contemporary nurses as an instance of their failure to cohere as a profession, failing to see their high turnover and frequent abandonment of their calling as a natural consequence of what he himself calls their disfranchisement within hospitals,[15] their usually very low pay and demanding working conditions, and their unwritten but strongly enforced duty to cover up the errors of their superiors.[16] It was a very similar set of circumstances, after all, which led to the resignation of the sisters of St. John's House, and probably only the financial advantages belonging to their class position enabled them to continue as a sisterhood after the loss of their original sponsors. The dilemma faced by the sisterhood's paid nurses, forced to choose between their loyalties and their livelihood, was similar to those faced by many nurses today. Commitment alone could not have been the only factor they weighed in their decision, but the fact remains that if they resigned they did so, like the sisters, because of it, now because they lacked it.

It seems obvious that the status of nurses cannot rise independently of the status and wishes of doctors and equally obvious that the medical profession as a whole is satisfied with very unequal relations between the two groups. What is perhaps less obvious is that the concept of professional prestige is itself so arbitrary that no resolution of the dilemma is likely to occur without its transformation or abandonment—a significant change in the status of doctors as well as of nurses.[17]

Victorian nurses such as Miss Burt and the sisters of St. John's House achieved all of the hallmarks of a profession except its prestige, and had it not been for the status anxiety of the male medical profession they would almost certainly have been contented with that. They did in fact share the "strong humanitarian motives" the Simpsons impute to semiprofessionals and represent as intellectually inferior and in some way antagonistic to the true professional's "strong intrinsic commitment to specialized knowledge or skills,"[18] but so did their medical colleagues. Given these anomalies of identity, it would seem to be time and past time to question the traditional formulations of professional standing. As all medical patients know intuitively, after all, their needs include both humanity and expertise; it requires little additional thought to realize that the fragmentation of these qualities between different medical personnel, with the doctor providing only science and the nurse only sympathy, is itself neither humane nor scientific—in a hospital, where "attending" physicians in fact usually see individual patients for only a few minutes a day, the proportions are obviously absurd.

The position of nurses in hospitals throughout the day and night, often in the absence of physicians, has always made the principle that nurses act only on doctors' orders something of a fiction, as Sister Caroline made clear in her 1874 explanation to Lord Hatherley of the principles behind the selection of nurses for night duty. Responsible patient care required then as now trained and independent personnel at all times as well as at all levels of whatever medical hierarchy the hospital's staff was arranged in: this was "the work" to which the St. John's House sisters repeatedly expressed their primary loyalty. The objectives of the medical men were considerably more mixed: the relief of suffering and the curing of disease had to share their attention with fees and appointments, power and prestige, and the latter especially seems to have been, as it was the least immediately relevant issue, the greatest distraction. It was in the pursuit of prestige that medical patients became the "vicarious sufferers" through whom medical men might make their reputations.

Implicitly, any nurse who regarded the patients' well-being as the chief end of the hospital's work was thus potentially opposed to her medical superiors, but if patients were to have any rights, even any other identity than as Wace's "occasion for experiments and researches," it was primarily up to the nurses to safeguard them. As Florence Nightingale believed, the "interests of the sick" were best served not by peace but by "publicity and collision," however disagreeable.[19] Victorian nurses agreed, and, their commitment clear, were ready to risk the consequences. Their example deserves to be known not only for their sake but for the sake of health care today—potentially, we are all of us, even doctors, patients, in need not of alternating science and tenderness but of a humane expertise from every sort of medical worker we encounter, from the doctor to the laboratory technician. In any hospital stay, however, the majority of the personnel in charge of us will be nurses, and at that moment if never before we will hope to meet women and men who are independent, trained, and committed, not medical maids of all work.

Epilogue

Included in the bound volume of old St. John's House annual reports and other memorabilia of their founders, the Nursing Sisters of St. John the Divine have preserved a single loose sheet of paper in Sister Caroline's writing which constitutes in a sense her final report to the council. It begins by noting a resolution passed by the council on 26 January 1888:

> That after the lapse of nearly three years from the secession of the Sisters, the Council remain actuated by an earnest and sincere desire for a reconciliation with them in the interests of the work to which the Sisters have given so many proofs of their devotion—and they request Sir Edmund Hay-Currie, one of their own body and also of the Sisters' Council [at this point Sister Caroline has interjected a note: "This of course is a mistake as the Sisters N. S. S. J. D. object to a Council and have none Sir E. H. Currie's name is amongst their list of Patrons"] to enter into communication with the Rev. R. Rhodes Bristow with that end in view.

The council's old conviction that the sisters had left them unnecessarily and ought to submit in their own best interests to the government of a male council was clearly unchanged, and the sisters probably did not need to discuss the proposal at length before they returned their answer: "that the Community of the Nursing Sisters of S. John the Divine desire to express their appreciation of the motives which prompted the Council of St. John's House to invite their return to Norfolk Street but regret that in view of their own present organization and the great amount of work to which they now stand pledged, it is impossible for them to accept the proposal made."[1] The Nursing Sisters of St. John the Divine were in fact thriving, while St. John's House was already moribund, and the sisters' appreciation of their former council's motives no doubt included an awareness of this fact.

A further glimpse of the sisterhood comes in Sarah A. Tooley's 1906 book, *The History of Nursing in the British Empire*. Sister Caroline had retired as superior in 1894 but was still a member of the community and is described by Tooley as "in vigorous old age, . . . [with] an entertaining fund of reminiscence."[2] One of the latest nurses of the sisterhood to be added to its pension list was Nurse Coles, the "nice person" who had made the original complaint against Dr. Hayes and who had afterward refused to comply with Frere's appeal for loyalty. Tooley credits her with "thirty-eight years of conscientious and devoted service in her profession,"[3] which dates her career back to 1868, the same year Sister Aimee became sister-in-charge at King's College Hospital. At the time of her complaint, therefore, Nurse Coles had had fifteen years of hospital experience. She was unlikely to have misjudged what she saw.

Notes

Introduction

1   The Department of Health and Social Security is the body responsible for this advertisement and its distribution.

2   Quoted in M. Adelaide Nutting and Lavinia L. Dock, *A History of Nursing* (New York: G. P. Putnam's Sons, 1907), 3:33.

3   Phyllis Kritek and Laurie Glass, "Nursing: A Feminist Perspective," *Nursing Outlook* 26 (March 1978): 182.

4   Marion Ferguson, "Reflections on Teaching a History of Nursing—1," Occasional Papers, *Nursing Times*, 15 November 1979, 117. For Florence Nightingale's range of interests and activities, see Cecil Woodham Smith, *Florence Nightingale* (New York: McGraw Hill, 1951), also J. Elise Gordon, "Nurses and Nursing in Britain, 23; The Work of Florence Nightingale—III: Her Influence throughout the World," *Midwife and Health Visitor* 9 (1973): 17–22.

5   Marion Ferguson, "Reflections on Teaching a History of Nursing—2," Occasional Papers, *Nursing Times*, 22 November 1979, 121.

6   Malcolm S. Newby, "Problems of Teaching Nursing History—1," Occasional Papers, *Nursing Times*, 22 November 1979, 123.

7   Ibid.

8   Malcolm S. Newby, "Problems of Teaching Nursing History—2," Occasional Papers, *Nursing Times*, 29 November 1979, 127. Among recent studies drawing on primary sources to enrich contemporary knowledge of nursing history are Brian Abel-Smith, *A History of the Nursing Profession* (London: Heinemann, 1960), which focuses on "the 'politics' of general nursing from 1800 onwards" (xi); Winifred Hector, *The Work of Mrs. Bedford Fenwick and the Rise of Professional Nursing* (London: Royal College of Nursing and National Council of Nurses of the United Kingdom, 1973); Jean Donnison, *Midwives and Medical Men* (London: Heinemann, 1977); Mary Stocks, *A Hundred Years of District Nursing* (London: Allen and Unwin, 1960); Jo Manton, *Sister Dora* (London: Methuen, 1971); and Celia Davies, ed., *Rewriting Nursing History* (London: Croom Helm, 1980).

9   See Abel-Smith, *History*, passim; see also Barbara Ehrenreich and Dierdre English, *Witches, Midwives, and Nurses: A History of Women Healers* (Old

Westbury, N.Y.: Feminist Press, 1973), passim, and John Woodward, *To Do the Sick No Harm: A Study of the British Voluntary Hospital System to 1875* (London: Routledge and Kegan Paul, 1974), 29–35 for some investigative qualification to the accepted view.

10 Abel-Smith, *History*, 27. See also M. Jeane Peterson, *The Medical Profession in Mid-Victorian London* (Berkeley: University of California Press, 1978). An interesting analogy can be drawn between Victorian doctors and nurses on the one hand and contemporary scientists and engineers on the other: "when British scientists did venture to pronounce on engineering matters they . . . frequently made fools of themselves. . . . A characteristic of such men was an unpuncturable self-esteem which led them to persist in their folly no matter how many times the engineer proved them wrong." The effect of this uninformed contempt on the engineers was of course to create in them an equal contempt for pure science. L. T. C. Rolt, *Victorian Engineering* (Harmondsworth: Pelican, 1974), 179–80.

11 Ehrenreich and English, *Witches*, 36. Barbara Ehrenreich and Dierdre English's *For Her Own Good: 150 Years of the Experts' Advice to Women* (New York: Anchor, 1978) is an excellent study of the roles played by women as medical *patients*. Unfortunately, its sole reference to nurses (278–79) is derogatory, the myth of their docility remaining completely unquestioned.

12 Conflict, of course, was not absolutely inevitable. Alice Fisher (1839–1888) succeeded in effecting substantial reforms both at Addenbrooke's Hospital, Cambridge, and the Radcliffe Infirmary, Oxford, "with the *entire* support of the medical and surgical staff," but her biographer's comment—"That must surely be a unique experience"—reflects the much greater incidence of conflict and controversy. Zachary Cope, *Six Disciples of Florence Nightingale* (London: Pitman Medical Publishing Co., 1961), 66.

13 Annette Kolodny, *The Land before Her: Fantasy and Experience of the American Frontiers, 1630–1860* (Chapel Hill: University of North Carolina Press, 1984), xiii.

14 Abel-Smith, *History*, 19–20.

15 H. Marjorie Simpson, "The Influence of Professional Nursing on the Development of the Modern Hospitals," in F. L. Poynter, ed., *The Evolution of Hospitals in Britain* (London: Pitman Publishing Co., 1964), 250–51.

16 Margaret Lonsdale, *Sister Dora, a Biography*, 5th ed. (London: C. Kegan Paul, 1880), 73–74.

17 "Trained Nurses for the Sick Poor," *The Lancet*, 4 June 1881, 923.

18 The father-mother-child relation that sometimes seems emulated by doctors, nurses, and patients is analyzed by Eva Gamarnikow as inherent in the patriarchal division of labor in her essay "Sexual Division of Labour: The Case of Nursing," in Annette Kuhn and AnnMarie Wolpe, eds., *Feminism and Materialism: Women and Modes of Production* (London: Routledge and Kegan Paul, 1978).

19 *OED*, under the word "sister," sense d.

20 Lonsdale, *Sister Dora*, 53–54.
21 Ibid., 106.
22 F. K. Prochaska, *Women and Philanthropy in Nineteenth-Century England* (New York and Oxford: Oxford University Press, 1980), 1.
23 Quoted in Abel-Smith, *History*, 26, from St. Thomas's Hospital Archives v6/67.

Chapter One

1 M. Adelaide Nutting and Lavinia L. Dock, *A History of Nursing* (New York: G. P. Putnam's Sons, 1907), 2:82.
2 Quoted in L. R. Seymer, *A General History of Nursing* (London: Faber and Faber, 1932), 69–70.
3 Nutting and Dock, *History*, 2:84.
4 Ibid., 2:83.
5 Dr. F. Cartwright, *The Story of the Community of the Sisters of St. John the Divine* (Hastings: The Community, 1968[?]), 3.
6 *St. John's House League News* [sic] (November 1903): 126–27, quoted in Nutting and Dock, *History*, 2:90.
7 Quoted in Abel-Smith, *History*, 25, from St. Thomas's Hospital Archives 67/1.
8 Nutting and Dock, *History*, 2:89.
9 "King's College Hospital," *The Times* (London), 28 February 1857, 12.
10 *St. John's House League News* (October 1904): 184, quoted in Nutting and Dock, *History*, 2:90–91.
11 *The Times* (London), 28 December 1868, 8.
12 Cartwright, *Story*, 7.
13 Greater London Council Archives MS. H. I./ST/ SJ/ A2/ 2, Minute Book of the Council of St. John's House, July 1864–January 1876, 81, my italics. Hereafter referred to as Minute Book.
14 Ibid., 91.
15 Ibid., 94.
16 Ibid., 99.
17 Ibid., 107–8.
18 Frederick F. Cartwright, "Community of Saint Mary and St. John" (typescript). I am very grateful to Dr. Cartwright for a copy of this short paper and to the Sisters of the Community of St. Margaret, who now operate it, for showing me over St. Joseph's Hospital, including the chapel and the original motto of Sister Mary Jones painted on a wall near the entrance to it. The hospital occupies premises on Burlington Lane, Chiswick, which were opened by members of the original community in 1897, thirty years after their separation from St. John's House.
19 Cartwright, *Story*, 10–11.

Chapter Two

1 "Christmas Appeals," *The Times* (London), 22 December 1871, 10.
2 "King's College Hospital—Annual Meeting," *The Times* (London), 19 May 1870, 12.
3 King's College Hospital Committee of Management Minute Books, vol. 8, December 1869–October 1872, 89, 91, 100, King's College Hospital Library. Hereafter referred to as Committee of Management Minute Book.
4 Minute Book, 160–61.
5 Cartwright, *Story*, 11.
6 Committee of Management Minute Book, 8:259.
7 Ibid., 8:444, 455.
8 Ibid., 8:497–98.
9 Ibid., vol. 9, November 1872–August 1875, 168–69.
10 Ibid., 9:177.
11 Greater London Council Archives MS. H. I./ ST/ SJ/ A19/ 3, Lady Superior's Reports 1869–1885, 73–74. Hereafter referred to as Lady Superior's Reports.
12 Quoted by Major-General Sir H. C. B. Daubeny in a letter to *The Times* (London), 14 February 1874, 10.
13 "King's College Hospital and St. John's House," *The Times* (London), 14 February 1874, 6.
14 Committee of Management Minute Book, 9:182.
15 Ibid., 9:186.
16 Ibid., 9:189.
17 "Report on the Nursing Arrangements of the London Hospitals, III," *British Medical Journal*, 4 April 1874, 461.
18 Ibid., 461–62.
19 Letter, *The Times* (London), 16 February 1874, 10.
20 "King's College Hospital and St. John's House," 14 February 1874, 6.
21 *The Lancet*, 21 February 1874, 274.
22 Letter, *The Times* (London), 16 February 1874, 10.
23 Letter, *The Times* (London), 18 February 1874, 11.
24 Letter, *The Times* (London), 20 February 1874, 12, my italics.
25 Minute Book, 219.
26 Ibid., 217–18.
27 Ibid., 220, italics in original.
28 Ibid., 268.
29 Ibid., 269–70.
30 Ibid., 270–71.
31 Letter, *The Times* (London), 20 February 1874, 12.
32 Greater London Council Archives MS. H. I./ ST/ SJ/ A36/ 1/ 17, draft of a letter from Dr. Lionel S. Beale to W. H. Smith, undated but in reply to a letter from Smith dated 6 January 1874.
33 Frederick F. Cartwright, *Joseph Lister: The Man Who Made Surgery Safe* (London: Weidenfeld and Nicholson, 1963), 74.

34 Ibid., 75, but see also George Thomas Bettany, "Fergusson, Sir William," *DNB* (1938). Fergusson received his license to practice surgery in 1828, the year in which his principal teacher, Robert Knox, was implicated in the Burke and Hare scandal over the procurement of anatomical specimens by grave robbing and murder. Knox's apparent belief in the semidivine rights of surgeons was an extreme instance of the arrogance Cartwright represents as fairly typical of Edinburgh surgeons. His comments on Lister (whom he admires), a later opponent of the St. John's House sisters, will be cited in Chapter 9.

35 "King's College Hospital and St. John's House," *The Times* (London), 28 February 1874, 10. The incident is reported in the Committee of Management Minute Book, 9:212 as having occurred in December 1872, but it evidently rankled.

Chapter Three

1 *The Times* (London), 27 February 1874, 7.

2 James McMullen Rigg, "Palmer, Roundell, First Earl of Selborne," *DNB* (1938).

3 *The Times* (London), 28 February 1874, 6. The phrase "*imperium in imperio*" was to become a cliché in the nursing disputes of the next decade; it appears here for perhaps the first time.

4 "King's College Hospital and St. John's House," 28 February 1874, 10.

5 Minute Book, 276.

6 Ibid., 278.

7 *The Times* (London), 2 March 1874, 5.

8 Greater London Council Archives MS. H. I./ ST/ SJ/ A36/ 1/ 15.

9 Ibid., 17. Smith's letter and Beale's second letter are cataloged together.

10 Greater London Council Archives MS. H. I./ ST/ SJ/ A39/ 13, "King's College Hospital, 1874. Report of the Committee of Management on the Subject of Their Impending Separation from St. John's House, Ordered to be Printed and Circulated amongst the Governors by Resolution of the Committee, come to at a Special Meeting, 6th February, 1874," iii–x. Hereafter referred to as Report of the Committee.

11 Ibid., x. The report seems to use single quotation marks for emphasis.

12 Greater London Council Archives MS. H. I. ST/ SJ/ A39/ 20, "To the Right Honorable Lord Hatherley," 2.

13 Ibid., 6–7.

14 Ibid., 8–9.

15 Ibid., 9.

16 Minute Book, 284–85.

17 Lady Superior's Reports, 90–91.

18 "King's College Hospital and St. John's House," *The Times* (London), 4 May 1874, 9.

19   Ibid. This supporter of the sisters is probably identical with Sir William Heathcote (1820–1903), a high church Tory landowner near Winchester who was a neighbor and friend of John Keble and Charlotte M. Yonge, supporters of sisterhoods both.
20   Ibid.
21   *The Times* (London), 8 May 1874, 7.
22   Lady Superior's Reports, 96–99.
23   Minute Book, 301.
24   "King's College Hospital and St. John's House," *The Times* (London), 15 May 1874, 10.

Chapter Four

1   Patricia Branca, *Silent Sisterhood: Middle-Class Women in the Victorian Home* (London: Croom Helm, 1975), 63. Branca cites Charles Booth as the source of these statistics.
2   Dr. Vernon Coleman, "Early Nursing," *Nursing Mirror*, 24 April 1975, 72.
3   *The Times* (London), 3 October 1884, 9. See also Peterson, *Medical Profession*, for a very detailed study of the profession's numbers, influence, and status.
4   Quoted in Woodward, *To Do the Sick*, 83.
5   Charles Booth, *Life and Labour of the People of London* (London: Macmillan, 1896), 8:81–82.
6   Sir Edward Cook, *The Life of Florence Nightingale* (London: Macmillan, 1914), 2:445–50.
7   See Donnison, *Midwives*, for the story in full detail.
8   Stocks, *Hundred Years*, 119–20.
9   *The Times* (London), 27 February 1877, 9.
10   *The Times* (London), 28 June 1877, 9.
11   *The Times* (London), 14 April 1876, 7.
12   *The Times* (London), 21 February 1878, 9.
13   *The Times* (London), 5 October 1876, 9.
14   *The Lancet*, 13 January 1877, 62.
15   *The Lancet*, 17 August 1878, 227, italics in original.
16   Charlotte Fell-Smith, "Blackwell, Elizabeth," *DNB* (1912); Fanny Cecilia Johnson, "Anderson, Elizabeth Garrett," *DNB* (1927); Katharine Jex-Blake, "Jex-Blake, Sophia," *DNB* (1927).
17   *The Lancet*, 17 August 1878, 227.
18   *The Lancet*, 11 December 1880, 946–47.
19   Gamarnikow, "Sexual Division"; Bernard Semmel, review of Peterson, *Medical Profession*, in *American Historial Review* 84 (June 1979): 753.
20   Leonore Davidoff, "Class and Gender in Victorian England," in Judith L. Newton, Mary P. Ryan, and Judith R. Walkowitz, eds., *Sex and Class in Women's History* (London: Routledge and Kegan Paul, 1983), 21.

Chapter Five

1 Greater London Council Archives MS. H9/ G4/ A3/ 10, "Guy's Hospital Committees, 1870–1883," 349. Hereafter referred to as Guy's Hospital Committees.

2 *The Times* (London), 13 October 1880, 10.

3 Samuel Wilks and G. T. Bettany, *A Biographical History of Guy's Hospital* (London: Ward, Lock, Bowden and Co., 1892), 147.

4 Quoted in *The Times* (London), 27 January 1873, 6. See also George Fisher Russell Barker, "Lushington, Stephen," *DNB* (1927), for a description of Lushington's career. Its bold though perhaps unrealistic liberalism is perhaps best briefly exemplified by his introduction in Parliament of a bill proposing the abolition of capital punishment at the very early date of 1840.

5 Lady Superior's Reports, 29.

6 *British Medical Journal*, 27 December 1879, 1045.

7 *British Medical Journal*, 29 November 1879, 871.

8 *British Medical Journal*, 6 December 1879, 898.

9 Letter, *The Times* (London), 28 July 1880, 7.

10 *Guy's Hospital Gazette* "Centenary Edition" (1872): 128.

11 Margaret Lonsdale, "The Present Crisis at Guy's Hospital," *The Nineteenth Century* 7 (April 1880): 677–78.

12 J. Braxton Hicks, "On Nursing Systems," *British Medical Journal*, 3 January 1880, 11.

13 Lonsdale, "The Present Crisis," 682–83.

14 "Report on the Nursing Arrangements of the London Hospitals, II," *British Medical Journal*, 14 March 1874, 357.

15 Hicks, "On Nursing Systems," 11.

16 *British Medical Journal*, 10 January 1880, 73.

17 John E. Neale, "On Nursing Systems," *British Medical Journal*, 17 January 1880, 90, my italics.

18 *British Medical Journal*, 14 February 1880, 272.

19 "Nursing Difficulties," *British Medical Journal*, 21 February 1880, 290.

20 Katherine Williams, "Ideologies of Nursing: Their Meanings and Implications," Occasional Papers, *Nursing Times* 70 (1974): 50.

21 Lonsdale, "The Present Crisis," 682.

22 Florence Nightingale, *Notes on Different Systems of Nursing from Notes on Hospitals* (1863), repr. *Selected Writings of Florence Nightingale* (New York: Macmillan, 1954), 223. Nightingale took French hospitals, many of them run by the Roman Catholic church, as well as English ones within the scope of her survey, hence her references to nuns.

Chapter Six

1 According to a statement of the governors later reported in the *British Medical Journal*, "a prejudice had been raised throughout the hospital

against the matron a month before she came, viz., on September 26th [1879]," a claim that the editors neglected to deny even as they dismissed it as unimportant. *British Medical Journal*, 9 October 1880, 602.

2 Guy's Hospital Committees, 369–70. The date of this resolution was 14 April 1880.

3 *British Medical Journal*, 8 May 1880, 707.

4 Margaret Lonsdale, "Doctors and Nurses. III," *The Nineteenth Century* 7 (June 1880): 1108. The All Saints Sisterhood seems for the most part to have avoided crises in spite of its commitment to ritualism. "There is nothing in the history of U.C.H. [University College Hospital] comparable to the embittered quarrel which broke out in 1874 between the Committee of King's College Hospital and St. John's. Indeed, when All Saints was attacked in the press for refusing to engage nurses who were not members of the Church of England [1885–86] the authorities of University College Hospital declined to intervene, even though this decision lost the hospital several donations." S. W. F. Holloway, "The All Saints Sisterhood at University College Hospital, 1862–99," *Medical History* 3 (1959): 151. This episode will be discussed briefly in Chapter 13.

5 Lonsdale, *Sister Dora*, 21–22.

6 Lonsdale, "The Present Crisis," 684.

7 Ibid., 678.

8 H. C. Cameron, *Mr. Guy's Hospital, 1762–1948* (London: Longmans, Green and Co., 1954), 208. In one case at Guy's in 1878, "'Maria Grant, a nurse-probationer from Job Ward, absconded from the Hospital on Thursday last with money to the account [sic] of 27 shillings belonging to 3 of the patients. She was apprehended on Monday and found to have pawned one of the Hospital dresses. . . . 'Diary of J. S. Steele, Superintendent, Guy's Hospital, . . . 22 May 1878," quoted in Woodward, *To Do the Sick*, 172. Such is the lingering prejudice against Miss Burt and her reforms that Woodward refers to this incident as evidence that the *new* nurses were not "perfect," even though it occurred at least a year before the reforms began, well prior to Miss Burt's arrival, and indeed supports *her* charges.

9 Cameron, *Mr. Guy's Hospital*, 218. Cameron was born in 1878 and presumably attended Guy's late in the 1890s, when many of the principals in the case were still alive and active. The great dispute was apparently not so long ago that they could look back on it with equanimity.

10 "Guy's Hospital," *British Medical Journal*, 24 July 1880, 144.

11 Margaret Lonsdale, Letter, *The Times* (London), 28 July 1880, 7.

12 Lonsdale, "The Present Crisis," 683.

13 William W. Gull, "The Nursing Crisis at Guy's Hospital. I," *The Nineteenth Century* 7 (May 1880): 887. Sir William Gull (1816–1890) is described in the *DNB* as "less popular among the leaders of his profession than with his patients . . . [and] prone . . . to tilt against current dogmas" and these qualities are evident in the rather eccentric role he chose to play in the nursing crisis, both in his reply to Lonsdale and in his testimony in the

Ingle case (see Chapter 7). He was one of the first nineteenth-century physicians to become strikingly wealthy, a fact which probably contributed to his independent attitude. G. T. Bettany, "Gull, Sir William," *DNB* (1917).

14 S. O. Habersohn, "The Nursing Crisis at Guy's Hospital. II," *The Nineteenth Century* 7 (June 1880): 898.

15 Ibid., 900–901, italics in original.

16 Alfred G. Henriques, "The Nursing Crisis at Guy's Hospital. III," *The Nineteenth Century* 7 (June 1880): 1904.

17 Seymour J. Sharkey, "Doctors and Nurses. II," *The Nineteenth Century* 7 (June 1880): 1104.

18 Octavius Sturges, "Doctors and Nurses. I," *The Nineteenth Century* 7 (June 1880): 1093–94.

19 Norman Moore, "Moxon, Walter," *DNB* (1917); Wilks and Bettany, *Biographical History*, 279–82.

20 *British Medical Journal*, 31 July 1886, 235.

21 Wilks and Bettany, *Biographical History*, 297–98.

22 Quoted in *British Medical Journal*, 31 July 1886, 235. These comments were written earlier than those in Wilks and Bettany, *Biographical History*; in the latter, Wilks more discreetly described the breakdown of Moxon's health in minute detail but calls his death merely "sudden and unanticipated" (298).

23 Margaret Lonsdale, Letter, *The Times* (London), 28 July 1880, 7.

24 Walter Moxon, Letter, *The Times* (London), 29 July 1880, 10.

25 Margaret Lonsdale, Letter, *The Times* (London), 2 August 1880, 10.

26 Ibid.

27 Walter Moxon, Letter, *The Times* (London), 5 August 1880, 6.

28 Walter Moxon, "Miss Lonsdale on Guy's Hospital," *Contemporary Review* 37 (1880): 874.

29 Lonsdale, "Doctors and Nurses," 1108.

30 "Lady Nurses," *Medical Times and Gazette*, 8 May 1880, 506.

Chapter Seven

1 Cameron, *Mr. Guy's Hospital*, 207.

2 "Guy's Hospital," *British Medical Journal*, 24 July 1880, 144.

3 Ibid., 144–45.

4 Ibid., 145.

5 Greater London Council Archives MS. H9/ G4/ A1/ 3, "Report of a Committee," 4. This part of the report is omitted from the *British Medical Journal*'s account.

6 "Guy's Hospital," *British Medical Journal*, 31 July 1880, 170.

7 Samuel Wilks, Letter, *The Times* (London), 23 July 1880, 7. This was the first time the matron's name had been given publicly. It is later than Lonsdale's *Nineteenth Century* articles but precedes her correspondence in the *Times* with Dr. Moxon.

8 Ibid.
9 S. O. Habersohn, Letter, *The Times* (London), 24 July 1880, 19.
10 "Charge against a Guy's Hospital Nurse," *The Times* (London), 27 July 1880, 12.
11 Cameron, *Mr. Guy's Hospital*, 213–14.
12 Ibid., 213. Dr. Pavy's distinction lay in his specialized studies of diabetes, a condition from which Morgan did not suffer.
13 *The Times* (London), 7 August 1880, 9.
14 Margaret Lonsdale, Letter, *The Times* (London), 28 July 1880, 9.
15 A letter to *The Times* (London), 12 August 1880, 11, from Hawkesley Rooke Hayes of Basingstoke Cottage Hospital testified to deficiencies in her earlier career, but not in time to do any good.
16 Cameron, *Mr. Guy's Hospital*, 213.
17 *The Times* (London), 7 August 1880, 9.
18 F. W. Pavy, Letter, *The Times* (London), 7 August 1880, 9.
19 Walter Moxon, Letter, *The Times* (London), 16 August 1880, 11.
20 Guy's Hospital Committees, 392–93.

Chapter Eight

1 *The Times* (London), 17 September 1880, 4.
2 *The Times* (London), 1 October 1880, 10.
3 *The Times* (London), 8 October 1880, 7.
4 Quoted in Cameron, *Mr. Guy's Hospital*, 211.
5 "Guy's Hospital," *British Medical Journal*, 16 October 1880, 626–27.
6 "The Imbroglio at Guy's," *Medical Times and Gazette* 16 (October 1880): 463.
7 *The Times* (London), 18 October 1880, 9.
8 *British Medical Journal*, 23 October 1880, 668.
9 Greater London Council Archives MS. H9/ G4/ A1/ 3, "Guy's Hospital General Court Minutes from 1860 to 1881," 236. Hereafter referred to as General Court Minutes.
10 "The Resignation of Dr. Habersohn and Mr. Cooper Forster," *Medical Times and Gazette*, 20. November 1880, 591.
11 Letter, *British Medical Journal*, 29 November 1880, 865–66.
12 "The Resignation," 592.
13 General Court Minutes, 236.
14 "Guy's Hospital," *British Medical Journal*, 25 December 1880, 1035.
15 "Guy's Hospital," *British Medical Journal*, 15 January 1881, 101.
16 Wilks and Bettany, *Biographical History*, 195.
17 "Guy's Hospital," *British Medical Journal*, 19 March 1881, 438.
18 "Guy's Hospital," *Medical Times and Gazette*, 9 April 1881, 403.
19 "Guy's Hospital," *British Medical Journal*, 27 August 1881, 368.
20 Guy's Hospital Committees, 429–30.

21 "Guy's Hospital," *British Medical Journal*, 27 August 1881, 368. For the testimonial, see "Guy's Hospital," *British Medical Journal*, 22 October 1881, 673.
22 "Hospital Death-Certificates," *British Medical Journal* 15 (July 1882): 103.
23 *The Times* (London), 10 October 1882, 10.
24 "The Charge against Hospital Authorities," *British Medical Journal*, 14 October 1882, 10.
25 Ibid.
26 "Guy's Hospital," *The Times* (London), 10 November 1882, 5.
27 "The Late Matron of Guy's Hospital," *British Medical Journal*, 9 December 1882, 1106.
28 Cameron, *Mr. Guy's Hospital*, 212, 218.
29 *The Times* (London), 20 December 1886, 9.
30 "Guy's Hospital," *The Times* (London), 21 December 1886, 8.

Chapter Nine

1 "Guy's Hospital," *British Medical Journal*, 27 August 1881, 368.
2 "Gamma," Letter, *British Medical Journal*, 6 March 1880, 389.
3 *The Lancet*, 11 June 1881, 958.
4 *The Lancet*, 13 January 1877, 62.
5 Letter, W. H. Smith to Lionel S. Beale, 6 January 1874, Greater London Council Archives MS. H. I./ ST/ SJ/ A36/ 1/ 17.
6 Minute Book, 317.
7 Ibid., 341.
8 Lady Superior's Reports, 109. The date of this report is 12 November 1875.
9 Greater London Council Archives H. I./ ST/ SJ/ A39/ 30, R. Few, *A History of St. John's House (Norfolk Street, Strand), With a Full Account of the Circumstances which Led to the Withdrawal Therefrom of the Entire Sisterhood, and A Refutation of the Charges Made Against the Sisters in the 'Statement' Issued by the Council on the 12th November and reiterated in the Letter of Mr. George William Bell (Honorary Secretary) dated the 31st December last* (London: W. Skeffington and Son, 1884), 18, Few's italics.
10 Committee of Management Minute Book, vol. 10, August 1875–July 1880, 319, 326.
11 Cartwright, *Joseph Lister*, 77.
12 Committee of Management Minute Book, 10:303, 326.
13 Sir Rickman John Goodlee, *Lord Lister* (Oxford: Oxford University Press, 1924), 410. Goodlee was both Lister's medical protégé and his nephew, and his biography is extremely admiring in tone. For evidence of professional dissension accompanying Lister's appointment, see "Professor Lister," *British Medical Journal*, 4 August 1877, 145–46, and "Professor Lister and Dr. Matthews Duncan," *British Medical Journal*, 6 October 1877, 489–90.
14 Cartwright, *Joseph Lister*.

15 Lady Superior's Reports, 128. The italics are Sister Caroline's; the date of the report is 16 October 1877.

16 Minute Book, 65, Sister Aimee's italics.

17 Goodlee, *Lord Lister*, 410–11.

18 Ibid., 410.

19 John Rudd Leeson, *Lister As I Knew Him* (London: Bailliere, Tindall and Cox, 1927), 187–88.

20 Goodlee, *Lord Lister*, 413.

21 Richard B. Fisher, *Joseph Lister, 1872–1912* (London: Macdonald and Jane's, 1977), 239.

22 Lady Superior's Reports, 134.

23 Committee of Management Minute Book, 10:498–99.

24 Committee of Management Minute Book, 10:499.

25 Greater London Council Archives MS. H. I./ ST/ SJ/ A33, *St. John's House and Sisterhood for the Training and Employment of Nurses for Hospitals, the Poor, and Private Families: Thirty-Second Annual Report of the Council for the Year Ending March 31, 1880* (London: Harrison and Sons, 1880) n.p.

26 Minute Book, 138.

27 Greater London Council Archives MS. H. I./ ST/ SJ/ A5/ 3, Minutes of the Meetings of the [St. John's] House Committee, December 1879–August 1884, 62. Hereafter referred to as Minutes of the Meetings.

28 Ibid., 62–63. Few's reply is dated 11 October 1882. Both letters appear in the house committee's minutes for 13 November.

29 Few, *A History*, 20–21, Few's italics.

30 Lady Superior's Reports, 184–85.

31 Ibid., 188–89.

32 Few, *A History*, 21–22, Few's italics.

33 Committee of Management Minute Book, 10:314.

34 Minute Book, 145.

35 King's College Hospital Medical School Library MS., "KCH Medical Board Minute Book," November 1879–November 1894, 164. Hereafter referred to as Medical Board Minute Book.

36 Lady Superior's Reports, 191.

37 Minute Book, 147.

Chapter Ten

1 Greater London Council Archives MS. H. I./ ST/ SJ/ A2/ 3, Council of St. John's House Minute Book, 1876–1913. The letter is pasted into the book at page 159. Hereafter referred to as Council Minute Book.

2 Ibid., 160.

3 Ibid., 160—Frere's printed letter.

4 Augustus Robert Buckland, "Jackson, John," *DNB* (1921).

5 Council Minute Book, 148.

6 Ibid., 149–50.

7 Ibid., 170.
8 Quoted in Fisher, *Joseph Lister*, 239. No source or date other than 1883 is given for this letter.
9 Few, *A History*, 18, Few's italics.
10 Council Minute Book, 150–51.
11 Ibid., 153.
12 Ibid., 151–52.
13 Ibid., 154.
14 Ibid., 162.
15 Ibid., 162.
16 Ibid.
17 Ibid.
18 Ibid., 163.
19 Ibid., 156–57.
20 Ibid., 170.
21 Ibid., 171–72.
22 Ibid., 172.
23 Medical Board Minute Book, 173.
24 Committee of Management Minute Book, Vol. 11, February 1880–May 1885, 355–56.
25 Council Minute Book, 185.
26 Lady Superior's Reports, 194.
27 "King's College Hospital," *The Times* (London), 4 May 1883, 10.

Chapter Eleven

1 Texts of the relevant letters are given most fully in Lady Superior's Reports, 197–99.
2 Council Minute Book, 178.
3 Ibid., 177–78.
4 Ibid., 196.
5 Ibid., 164–65.
6 Ibid., 186–87.
7 Ibid., 194. These recommendations were received at the council's meeting of 4 July 1883.
8 Minutes of the Meetings, 82; Few, *A History*, 32–33.
9 Council Minute Book, 202.
10 Ibid., 199.
11 Minutes of the Meetings, 98.
12 Ibid., 82.
13 Ibid., 83.
14 Quoted in Few, *A History*, 48–49, italics are probably Few's, not Sister Caroline's.
15 Minutes of the Meetings, 85–87.
16 Ibid., 80–81.

17 Greater London Council Archives MS. H. I./ ST/ SJ/ A34/ 2, "The Secretary's Letter Book, Out letters for June–December, 1883," 46. Hereafter referred to as Secretary's Letter Book.
18 Minutes of the Meetings, 146.
19 Ibid., 99. The letter from Bell to Nicolls cited here is not otherwise extant.
20 Ibid., 100–101.
21 Ibid., 101–3.
22 Ibid., 103.
23 "King's College Hospital," *The Times* (London), 21 July 1883, 14.
24 Lady Superior's Reports, 199.
25 Greater London Council Archives MS. H. I./ ST/ SJ/ A35/ 3, "In-letters, Feb. 1883–June, 1884," n.p.
26 Minutes of the Meetings, 81–82.
27 Few, *A History*, 53.

Chapter Twelve

1 Greater London Council Archives H. I./ ST/ SJ/ Y3/ 2, an untitled album of newspaper cuttings, n.p.
2 Greater London Council Archives H. I./ ST/ SJ/ A39/ S7, reprint from the *Guardian* of Bartle J. L. Frere's 4 August 1883 statement in defense of the council of St. John's House, 1–3.
3 Ibid., 5–6.
4 *The Times* (London), 8 August 1883, 10.
5 Minutes of the Meetings, 108.
6 Ibid., 112.
7 Lady Superior's Reports, 201.
8 Minutes of the Meetings, 114–15.
9 Ibid., 115.
10 Ibid., 116–17.
11 "The Sisterhood of St. John's House and King's College Hospital," *The Lancet*, 11 August 1883, 241.
12 "King's College Hospital and St. John's House," *Medical Times and Gazette*, 11 August 1883, 159.
13 Minutes of the Meetings, 118–19.
14 *The Times* (London), 20 August 1883, 3.
15 *The Times* (London), 18 August 1883, 3.
16 Included in the previously cited unpaged album of newspaper cuttings. This letter is quoted from *The Morning Post*, 21 August 1883.
17 The unpaged album of newspaper cuttings. The comment is from the *Church Times*, 21 August 1883.
18 Minutes of the Meetings, 136–37.
19 Ibid., 141–42. The date of this meeting was 12 September 1883.
20 Ibid., 146–47.
21 "The Nursing Sisters of St. John," *The Times* (London), 20 September 1883, 10.

22 Ibid.
23 Minutes of the Meetings, 150.
24 Ibid., 150–52.
25 Ibid., 175.
26 *The Lancet*, 29 September 1883, 551.
27 "Charing Cross Hospital and St. John's-House," *The Times* (London), 9 November 1883, 6.
28 Ibid.
29 Council Minute Book, 214–15.
30 "St. John's-House," *The Times* (London), 21 November 1883, 4. The full report is also available in the Greater London Council Archives, MS. H. I./ ST/ SJ/ A33.
31 Minutes of the Meetings, 181, italics in original.
32 "The St. John's Home," *The Times* (London), 26 November 1883, 7.
33 Few, *A History*, 39.
34 Minutes of the Meetings, 177–78.
35 Greater London Council Archives MS. H. I./ ST/ SJ/ A34/ 3, letter of 3 January 1884 from Ernest Frere to the bishop of Bedford.
36 Few, *A History*, 37–39, Few's italics.
37 Minutes of the Meetings, 207. The meeting was held 17 January 1884, five months after the sisters' departure.
38 "A Nursing Sisterhood," *The Times* (London), 6 December 1883, 3.
39 Greater London Council Archives MS. H. I./ ST/ SJ/ A31, "Confidential, For the use of Members of the Committee only," n.p.
40 "Nursing Sisters of St. John the Divine," *The Times* (London), 18 December 1883, 10.
41 Minutes of the Meetings, 189.
42 Ibid., 190.
43 Ibid., 191.
44 Few, *A History*, 42.
45 Minutes of the Meetings, 213–14.
46 Ibid., 218.
47 Nutting and Dock, *History*, 2:94; Seymer, *General History*, 70–71.
48 Cartwright, *Story*, passim.
49 Lady Superior's Reports, 209.
50 "Hospital Authorities and Nursing," *The Lancet*, 8 August 1885, 259.
51 "St. John's House," *The Guardian*, 15 August 1883, unpaged cutting included in the album cited above.
52 Few, *A History*, back cover.
53 Minute Book, 107, italics in original.

Chapter Thirteen

1 Cameron, *Mr. Guy's Hospital*, 14.
2 The initial course of the controversy may be followed in the *Times*

throughout the month of August 1886, and its resolution, when the Hospital Sunday Fund agreed to allocate money to the hospital, throughout the month of December. For the general history of the All Saints Sisterhood at University College Hospital, see Holloway, "All Saints Sisterhood," 46–56. For King's College Hospital's financial difficulties, see "King's College Hospital," *The Times* (London), 7 June 1884, 12, in which Lord Francis Hervey, chairman of the committee of management, published an appeal for funds which called the hospital's finances "straitened and even necessitous."

3 Lionel S. Beale, *Hospital Patients, Doctors, and Nurses: A Lecture* (London: J. and A. Churchill, 1874), 21.

4 "Nursing Sisterhoods," *British Medical Journal*, 18 August 1883, 345–46.

5 "King's College Hospital," *The Times* (London), 2 October 1884, 9.

6 *The Times* (London), 3 October 1883, 9.

7 "British Medical Association," *The Times* (London), 11 August 1886, 8.

8 "The Imbroglio at Guy's," *Medical Times and Gazette*, 16 August 1880, 463.

9 Branca, *Silent Sisterhood*, 71–72. See also Ehrenreich and English, *For Her Own Good*, passim.

10 "British Medical Association."

11 Reprinted in the column "*JAMA* 100 Years Ago," *JAMA*, 5 September 1986, 1134. I am indebted to Dr. Martin Palmer for this reference.

12 *The Lancet*, 5 March 1881, 379, italics in original. See also *The Lancet*, 9 May 1874, 663–64 and 20 June 1874, 880–81. The coincidence of dates between the nursing controversies and *The Lancet's* editorializing on the proper role of women is probably significant.

13 *The Lancet*, 11 March 1876, 397–98, my italics.

14 "The Week. Topics of the Day," *Medical Times and Gazette*, 9 July 1881, 42.

15 Brian Harrison, *Separate Spheres: The Opposition to Women's Suffrage in Britain* (New York: Holmes and Meier, 1978), 75, 194. For the substance of Wright's attack, see Carol Bauer and Lawrence Ritt, eds., *Free and Ennobled: Source Readings in the Development of Victorian Feminism* (Oxford: Pergamon Press, 1979), 262–65.

16 Harrison, *Separate Spheres*, 188.

17 Cameron, *Mr. Guy's Hospital*, 4. See also Peterson, *Medical Profession*, especially Chapter 4, "Formation of a Professional Elite," passim.

18 H. E. Counsell, quoted in Peterson, *Medical Profession*, 88. Counsell, whose memoirs were not published until 1943, was a student at Guy's during the nursing controversy. While his recollections are in some points inaccurate (for example, see his statements that the entire nursing staff was dismissed and that "the excitement lasted about a week"), his belief that "many of the nurses were in reality members of a much older though less distinguished profession" and that this fact accounted for the loyalty of "many of the students" may well be true: it was an aspect of the situation that would not have been alluded to publicly at the time, no matter how many people were aware of it. H. E. Counsell, *37 the Broad, The Memoirs of an Oxford Doctor* (London: Robert Hale Ltd., 1943), 11.

19 Peterson, *Medical Profession*, 274.

Chapter Fourteen

1 Amitai Etzioni, ed., Preface, *The Semi-Professions and Their Organization: Teachers, Nurses, Social Workers* (New York: The Free Press, 1969), xv. This is precisely the sort of argument which led Wilma Scott Heide, former president of the National Organization for Women and a nurse with an advanced degree in sociology as well, to conclude that nurses need even more than most women to identify themselves as feminists: the convenience of labeling them as feminine otherwise consistently leads to their dismissal as experts or decision makers. Wilma Scott Heide, "Nursing and Women's Liberation," *American Journal of Nursing* 73 (1973): 824.

2 Etzioni, ed., *The Semi-Professions*, vi–vii. The language of this passage, including the incidental racism implicit in the allusion to "passing," makes clear the writers' assumption that they necessarily understand their subjects' situations better than the subjects themselves and are competent to prescribe behavior for them.

3 Ida Harper Simpson and Richard Simpson, "Women and Bureaucracy in the Semi-Professions," in ibid., 231–32.

4 Ibid., 198.

5 Jo Ann Ashley, *Hospitals, Paternalism, and the Role of the Nurse* (New York: Teachers College Press, 1976), 17.

6 Fred E. Katz, "Nurses," in Etzioni, ed., *The Semi-Professions*, 56, my italics.

7 Patricia Cayo Sexton, *The New Nightingales: Hospital Workers, Unions, New Women's Issues* (New York: Enquiry Press, 1982), passim.

8 Katz, "Nurses," 56.

9 Ibid., 56.

10 Ibid., 59–60.

11 Ibid., 70.

12 William J. Goode, "The Theoretical Limits of Professionalization," in Etzioni, ed., *The Semi-Professions*, 280.

13 Ibid., 267.

14 Ibid., 288.

15 Katz, "Nurses," 70.

16 Sexton, *New Nightingales*, passim.

17 Evaluating the status of American nurses in the twentieth century, Barbara Melosh concludes that "within the existing division of labor, nursing is not a profession, because nurses' autonomy is constrained by medicine's professional dominance. In broader cultural terms, nursing by definition cannot be a profession because most nurses are women." Melosh, *"The Physician's Hand": Work Culture and Conflict in American Nursing* (Philadelphia: Temple University Press, 1982), 20. It is the acceptance of such patterns of irrational dominance as definitive, not Melosh's analysis of how they operate in practice, that this chapter attempts to challenge.

18 Simpson and Simpson, "Women and Bureaucracy," 203, 199.

19 Nightingale, *Notes*, 223.

Epilogue

1 This paper is among the uncataloged records in the possession of the Nursing Sisters of St. John the Divine at their mother house in Birmingham.
2 Sarah A. Tooley, *The History of Nursing in the British Empire* (London: S. H. Bousfield and Co., 1906), 73.
3 Ibid., 74.

INDEX

Abel-Smith, Brian, xii
Abram, Edward, 156
Acland, Sir Thomas, 75
All Saints Sisterhood, 64, 164, 169–70, 198 (n. 4)
Almack, Edward, 104, 107, 129–30, 131, 136
Anderson, Elizabeth Garrett, 47
Ashley, Jo Ann, 182
Authority, xi–xiv, 8, 12–13, 44–45, 101–2, 107, 112–13, 141–42; at issue at King's College Hospital in 1874, 16, 29–30, 49, 126–27, 129–30; at issue in nursing systems, 56–57, 58–60

Barry, Alfred, 36–37
Baxter, E. Buchanan, 117
Beale, Lionel S., 8, 23, 27–29, 38, 102, 119, 170–71, 179, 180
Bedford, Bishop of, 157, 159–60, 162
Bedwell, F. A., 27
Bell, George William, 112, 115, 119, 120, 123, 133, 140, 141, 158, 159–60, 161
Blackwell, Elizabeth, 47
Blyth, James S., 6–7
Booth, Charles, 41
Boucherett, L.: letter to Florence Nightingale, xvi–xvii
Bowman, Sir William, 119, 122, 131, 136, 142, 172
Branca, Patricia, 174
Bristow, R. Rhodes, 188

British Medical Association, 47, 173
British Medical Journal, 63, 64, 69, 77, 87, 88, 90, 92, 93–94, 95, 96; "Report on the Nursing Arrangements of the London Hospitals," 17–18, 58; reports on Guy's Hospital, 55, 59; "On Nursing Systems," 56–57; letters, 60, 90, 91, 101–2, 171–72
British Nurses' Association, ix
Burt, Margaret, 54, 56, 64, 67, 74, 79, 80, 81, 87–88, 92, 93, 94, 101, 102, 169, 177, 182, 199 (n. 7); appointed matron of Guy's Hospital, 53, 197–98 (n. 1); at Leicester Infirmary, 55, 57, 59, 60; opposition at Guy's, 55–56; changes initiated at Guy's, 65–66, 70; exonerated by Guy's Board of Governors, 75–77, 84–85; resignation, 95–96
Butler, Henry E., 156

Cambridge, Duke of, 25, 36
Cameron, H. C., 65–66, 75–76, 80, 81, 95–96, 169, 177, 178, 198 (n. 9)
Cartwright, Frederick F., 23, 39; *Story of the Community of the Nursing Sisters of St. John the Divine*, 13–14
Charing Cross Hospital, 7, 124, 149, 156; health problems of staff in 1882, 111–12, 113; problems with St. John's House, 155–56, 157–58
Christianity: inspirational value to

Christianity (*continued*)
Victorian nurses, xiv–xv;
subversive influence on nurses, 57,
66, 108
Church Times, 155, 162
Clark, Andrew, 177
Class: importance of, in nineteenth-
century nursing disputes, xi–xii,
50, 136
Coles, Nurse (King's College
Hospital), 125, 138, 189
Committee of Management of King's
College Hospital, 12, 15, 16, 20, 26–
27, 29, 31, 37–38, 49, 121–22, 129
Contemporary Review, 63
Cook, Sir Edward, 41
Cooper Forster, John, 86–87, 89–92
Council of St. John's House, 12, 15,
27, 29, 33–34, 116, 117, 118–89;
dispute with Sisterhood in 1883,
122–32 passim, 135–36, 141–46;
acceptance of Sister Caroline's
resignation, 132; publicly
criticized, 147; charges against
sisters, 159, 161–62
Counsell, H. E., 206 (n. 18)
Curnow, John, 117

Daubeny, Major General Sir Charles,
16, 17, 18, 19, 21, 26, 27, 36, 74
Davidoff, Leonore, 49
Davies-Colley (surgeon at Guy's
Hospital), 75
Dickens, Charles, xi
Duckworth, G. H., 41
Duffin, Alfred Baynard, 23, 106, 107,
125
Duncan, Andrew, 14

Ehrenreich, Barbara, xii
Eliot, George, xiii
English, Dierdre, xii
Ericksen, J. E., 41
"Espionage," 58, 59–60, 66, 126
Etzioni, Amitai, 180, 181

Feminism: response to nursing, x,
xii, 207 (n. 1)
Fenwick, Ethel Gordon, ix
Ferguson, Marion, xi
Fergusson, Sir William, 23, 24, 39,
103–4, 195 (n. 34)
Few, Robert, 9, 104, 112, 115, 119,
135, 145–46, 156, 157–58, 159, 160–
61, 163, 164
Forster, Edward M., 102, 103–4, 114
Frere, Bartle, 104, 111, 118–19, 122,
123, 124–25, 126–27, 133–34, 144–
45, 147–56, 158–59, 177, 189;
appeal to nurses at King's College
Hospital, 138, 141–42
Frere, Elizabeth, 4
Frere, Ernest, 150

Galton, *Hereditary Genius*, 175
Gamarnikow, Eva, 48
Garrod, A. B., 23
Gender: in nursing controversies, ix–
x, 41–42, 101–2, 171–72, 176–77; in
professional status, 180–87
Gibbs, Henry Hucks, 86
Girdlestone, Sister Laura, 9, 165
Gladstone, William Ewart, 25
Glass, Laurie, x, xi
Goode, William J., 184–85
Goodlee, Sir Rickman John, 107, 108,
201 (n. 13)
Guardian (newspaper), 147, 162, 164
Gull, Sir William, 67, 80, 81, 82, 97,
179, 198–99 (n. 13)
Guy's Hospital, xi, xvii, 48, 53, 54,
59, 64, 65, 67, 69, 70, 71, 74, 80,
101, 102, 143, 150, 164, 169, 174,
178, 185; Court of Committees, 62,
82–83, 93; Board of Governors, 74,
76–77, 89; action of medical staff,
86; financial difficulties, 89, 96–97
Guy's Hospital Gazette, 54, 56, 89, 92

Habersohn, S. O., 67–68, 76, 78–79,
86–87, 89–92

Hatherley, Lord, 25, 26, 30, 35, 38, 186
Hay-Currie, Sir Edmund, 188
Hayes, Thomas Crawford, 115–16, 119–21, 125, 131, 132, 138, 141, 146, 159, 184, 189
Heide, Wilma Scott, 207 (n. 1)
Henriques, Alfred G., 68
Hicks, J. Braxton, 56–57, 58, 59, 91
Hodson, Mrs. (superior of St. John's House), 10, 163
Hospital for Sick Children, Nottingham, 7
Hospitals, xiii–xv, 43, 48–49, 111–12, 182–84, 187; patients in, xiii, xvi, 6, 14, 110, 178–79, 182–84, 186–87
House Committee of St. John's House, 135, 137, 138, 139, 140, 142, 146, 149, 150, 156, 157, 160, 162, 164
Howard, Nurse Adeline, 137, 139, 143, 156, 161
Hunt, Agnes, xiii

Iliff, William T., 84
Ingle, Nurse Pleasance Louisa, 78, 79–80, 81, 82

Jackson, John, 121, 137
Jex-Blake, Sophia, 47
Johnson, George, 23
Jones, Sister Mary, 5–6, 12, 13, 163; resignation, 8–10, 133; foundation of the Sisterhood of St. Mary and St. John, 10
Journal of American Medicine, 176

Katz, Fred E., 182–84, 185
King's College, 172
King's College Hospital, xi, xvii, 20, 25, 39, 49, 55, 57, 69, 101, 102, 153, 169, 170, 185, 189; appeals for funds, 6–7, 11; contracts with St. John's House, 6, 17, 20, 38, 107; governance, 16; cost of nursing,
17–19, 21; medical staff in 1874, 22–24; appointment of Joseph Lister, 104–5; governors praise St. John's House, 111; health problems of staff in 1882, 111–12, 113; medical staff in 1883, 116–17; separation from St. John's House, 124, 149, 164; conditions of work in 1883, 133; value to St. John's House, 134; nurses at, in 1883, 138
Kolodny, Annette, xii
Kritek, Phyllis, x, xi

The Lancet, 49, 56, 65, 78; quoted, xiv, 19, 45–47, 47–48, 102, 152, 157, 164, 176, 181
Lawrence, Sir Trevor, 90
Leicester Infirmary, 55, 57, 59, 60
Lister, Sir Joseph, 23, 106, 107, 114, 117, 122, 131, 142, 146, 172; appointment to King's College Hospital, 104–5; conflict with St. John's House Sisters, 106–10; attitude toward women, 109
Lloyd, Sister Caroline, 15, 16, 21, 39, 54, 103, 105, 135, 141, 150, 162, 163, 186, 188–89; appointed superior of St. John's House, 12; letter to Lord Hatherley, 30–33; reports to St. John's House Council, 34–35, 37, 109, 113, 116, 117, 123–24; on leave, 121; resignation as superior, 132; support of the Sisterhood, 136; letter to King's College Hospital nurses, 137–38; departure from St. John's House, 143, 145, 149, 151–53, 159–60; letter to the Bishop of Bedford, 159–60
Loag, Mary Elizabeth, 53
London Hospital, 68, 177
London School of Medicine for Women, 47
Lonsdale, Margaret, 69, 77, 78, 81, 88, 184; Sister Dora, A Biography, xvi; letters to the Times, 55, 70–71;

Lonsdale, Margaret (*continued*)
"The Present Crisis at Guy's
Hospital," 56, 57–58, 61, 63, 66, 67;
dispute with Moxon, 64, 70–74, 93
Lushington, Edmund, 53, 54, 55, 62,
76, 93, 96, 97
Lushington, Stephen, 54

Manning, Henry Edward, xiv
Marriott, C. H., 55, 59
Medical Times and Gazette, 74, 84,
89–90, 92–93, 152, 174
Medicine: as a profession, 41–50
passim, 171–73, 177–79, 186;
women in, 47, 176
Midwives' Registration Act, 42
Monro, Hector, 156, 158
Moore, Withers, 173, 175–76, 181
Morgan, Louisa, 78, 79–80, 81, 82,
179
Moxon, Walter, 75, 76, 82, 184;
dispute with Lonsdale, 64, 70–74,
93; death, 69

Neale, John E., 59
Newby, Malcolm S., xi, xii
Newman, John Henry, xiv
Nicolls, Major General J. E. T., 132–
33, 140, 159
Nightingale, Florence, x, xiii, xv,
xvii, 41, 61–62, 68, 187; letter to
Mary Jones, 5
Nightingale School for Nurses, 47
Nineteenth Century, 63, 65, 69, 73, 78
Nurses, 3–4; as servants, xiii–xiv, 48–
49; as staff at King's College
Hospital, 22; change in class, 41–
42, 170–71; character
requirements, 43–45; unreformed
at Guy's Hospital, 54, 56, 66–67;
new regulations at Guy's, 85;
position in King's College Hospital,
127, 129, 136; St. John's House,
136–39, 150–51; in hospital caste
systems, 182–83

Nursing: as a calling for women, ix–
x, xvi, 44–47; history of, x–xi,
xvii; by sisterhoods, 58, 59;
professional status of, 170–71, 186–
87, 207 (n. 17); as a "semiprofession," 180
Nursing Sisters of St. John the
Divine, 154, 156, 160, 164–65, 169,
188–89

Oxford University, 73

Paget, Sir James, 41
Parry, Sister Aimee, 21, 22, 26, 29–30,
37, 38, 49, 101, 103, 107, 113, 150,
160, 163, 177, 182, 184; appointed
sister in charge at King's College
Hospital, 12; character questioned
by Cartwright, 13–15, 39; defended
by Sister Caroline, 15, 32–33, 117;
letters from, 21–22, 105–6, 109–10,
122, 128, 130, 139–40, 154;
appointed sister matron at King's
College Hospital, 38; conflict with
King's College Hospital medical
staff, 109–10, 114–15, 120–21, 145;
work praised, 111, 113, 128;
conflict with St. John's House
Council, 116, 132–33; supported by
Sisterhood, 117, 136, 155; opposed
by Bartle Frere, 120–21, 122, 123,
124–25, 126–27, 141–42, 144, 146–
49, 151, 153–54, 158–59; appointed
acting superior of St. John's House,
121; departure from King's College
Hospital, 126, 127–28; accused of
subverting King's College Hospital
nurses, 137; attacked by Nurse
Howard, 139; praised by *Church
Times*, 155
Pattison, Dorothy. *See* Sister Dora of
Walsall
Pattison, Mark, xiii
Pavy, F. W., 75, 79, 80, 81, 82, 97, 179
Peterson, M. Jeane, 48

Playfair, W. S., 23, 115–16
Prince of Wales, 97, 130–31
Prochaska, F. K., xvi
Professionalization, 170–71, 179, 184–87
Pye-Smith, P. H., 75

Robinson, Randolph, 11, 19, 21, 29, 111, 114, 119
Rothschild, Leopold de, 97
Royal Infirmary (Edinburgh), 106

St. Bartholomew's Hospital, 41
St. John's House, 11, 47, 54, 55, 69, 101, 131, 169, 182, 186, 187, 188–89; foundation, 3–4; at King's College Hospital, 6, 12, 17–21, 31–33, 39, 101–4, 133, 161–62, 164; at Charing Cross Hospital, 7, 155–56; dispute with Council in 1868, 7–10; constitutional question, 12–13, 135; support for Sister Aimee in 1874, 22–23; and Joseph Lister, 105–11; dissolution of, 124; support for Sister Aimee in 1883, 127–28; resignation of Sisters in 1883, 134–35; public support for Sisters, 147; difficulties of Council, 155–56, 157–58; failure to recover after secession of Sisters, 164
St. Joseph's Hospital, 10
St. Saviour's Board of Guardians, 84
St. Thomas's Hospital, 47, 68, 164
Selborne, Lord, 25–26, 35, 38
Semmel, Bernard, 49
Sharkey, Seymour J., 68
Simpson, Ida Harper, 181–82, 186
Simpson, Richard, 181–82, 186
Sister Aimee. See Parry, Sister Aimee
Sister Caroline. See Lloyd, Sister Caroline
Sister Clinical (Guy's Hospital), 93–94
Sister Dora of Walsall, xiii, xv–xvi, 64–65

Sisterhood of St. Mary and St. John, 10
Sisterhood of the Good Samaritan, xv
Sister Isabel (King's College Hospital), 133, 136, 137
Sisters' Fund, 159, 160, 163
Smith, Henry, 24
Smith, W. H., 23, 27–29, 102
Society of Apothecaries, 47
Spencer, Herbert, 175
Steele, J. C., 75–76, 96
Stewart, John, 106–7
Sturges, Octavius, 68

Tait, Archibald Campbell, 7, 8–9
Thermometer: use of, by nurses, 60–61
Times (London), 62, 76, 80, 156, 162, 173; quoted, 16, 18–19, 25, 26, 38, 40, 43–45, 81, 82, 89, 94, 96–97, 130–31, 143, 150, 161; letters quoted, 22, 27, 37, 53–54, 70-71, 77–79, 84–86, 152, 153–54
Tompson, Dr. (house physician at King's College Hospital), 125
Tooley, Sarah A., 189
Turner, Thomas, 53
TV Times, ix

University College Hospital, 41, 64, 169
University of London, 69
University of Wisconsin-Milwaukee, x

Wace, Henry, 172–73, 187
Waddell, James, 156
Walrond, J. C., 16, 17, 20, 23, 26, 31–32, 33–34, 39, 102, 107
Westhorpe, Richard, 155
Westminster Hospital, 59, 68
Wilbraham, Sir Richard, 125–26
Wilks, Samuel, 70, 77, 90–91
Williams, Katherine, 60–61
Women: innately subordinate, 148–

Women (*continued*)
  49, 153–54, 176–77, 180–82; higher
  education opposed, 173; medical
  knowledge of, in 1880s, 174–76;
  medical study by, opposed, 176–77

Wood, John, 23
Wordsworth, Christopher (Bishop of
  Lincoln), 111, 119, 157
Wright, Almroth, 177